Welcome to the Awesome Anatomy Co. Guide to musculoskeletal anatomy! This book has been a true labour of love and I really hope you enjoy reading this. I also hope it helps to make things a little easier for your studies, or if you are just wishing to understand human musculoskeletal anatomy better!

Thank you so much for supporting me and my dreams,

Sophie x

CONTENTS PAGE

Chapter 5: The Elbow joint

Chapter 6: The Forearm

Chapter 7: The Wrist joint

Chapter 12: The Hip

Chapter 13: The Knee

Chapter 14: The Leg/Calf

Chapter 15: The Ankle

Chapter 16: The Foot

Chapter 17: The Lower limb nerves (the lumbar, lumbosacral, and sacral plexuses)

Chapter 18: The blood supply of the lower limb

Chapter 19: The Trunk and neck

Chapter 22: The Skull

Chapter 23: The Mandible and Hyoid

Chapter 24: The Answers

Chapter 25: References

CHAPTER ONE

OVERVIEW OF BASIC ANATOMY PRINCIPLES

THE ANATOMICAL POSITION:

The anatomical position is described as the body standing erect and facing forwards, the legs together with the feet parallel and toes pointing forwards. The arms are described as hanging loosely to the sides of the body, with the palms facing forwards and thumbs facing laterally.

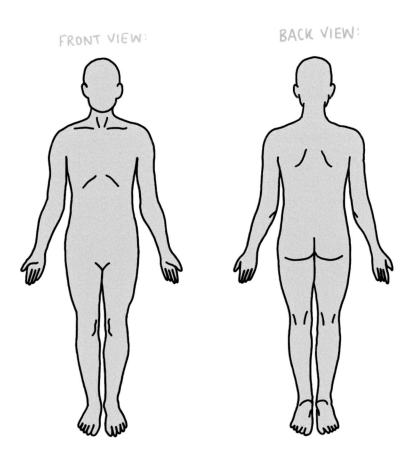

Figure 1. Illustration of the anatomical position, front, and back view.

The anatomical position is used as a "neutral" position when assessing anatomy. It can also be used when assessing patients, such as during an observation, to check for any differences in appearance of particular areas of the body. It is a good position to be able to compare the body bilaterally, e.g., to compare an injured shoulder against an uninjured shoulder.

QUICK FIRE QUIZ! (You may need to use knowledge from the next few pages to answer this question!)

In the anatomical position which direction are the palms facing?

A. Anteriorly
B. Posteriorly
C. Superiorly

(Answers are revealed at the back of the book!)

PLANES AND AXIS OF THE HUMAN BODY:

Now we have covered the anatomical position we can move onto the planes and axis of the human body! We can divide the human body up into several different planes and axis. Let us start with the planes.

Sagittal plane: A plane which divides the body in half down the midline, into both left and right halves.

Parasagittal plane: A plane which is parallel to the sagittal plane but does not sit directly on the midline of the body.

Frontal (coronal) plane: A plane which divides the body into anterior and posterior parts (This plane is perpendicular to the sagittal plane).

Transverse plane (horizontal): A plane which divides the body in half horizontally into inferior and superior parts (This plane is perpendicular to both the sagittal and frontal planes).

Now we have covered the planes, lets us move onto the axis...

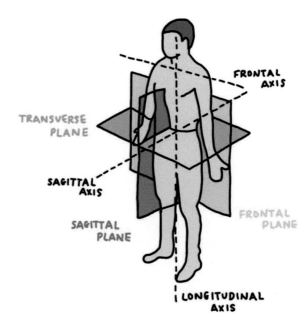

Figure 2. An illustration of the planes and axis of the body.

Frontal axis: An axis whereby movements occur in the direction of either anterior or posterior motions (e.g. Doing a forward or backward somersault!)

Sagittal axis: An axis whereby movement occurs in either the direction of lateral or medial motions (e.g. Completing a cartwheel).

Longitudinal axis: An axis whereby movement occurs around the midline of the body. (e.g. Spinning around in a circle).

MOVEMENT TERMS:

Here are a couple of movement related terms that will be useful to know!

AROM (Active range of motion): Active movement of joint (patient completes).

PROM (Passive range of motion): Light pressure applied to end feel of joint.

RROM (Resisted range of motion): Patient resists active movements.

End feel: The furthest physiological range a joint can be taken to.

QUICK FIRE QUIZ! (Answers are at the back of this book!)

What sections does the frontal (coronal) plane divide the body into?

   A. Lateral and medial
   B. Anterior and Superior
   C. Sagittal and transverse

ANATOMICAL TERMS:

So now you've got an understanding of the orientation of the human body, lets look a little deeper at some anatomical terms you will likely use during your studies, so make sure to learn these well!

Anterior (ventral): To the front of / in front of eg. The knee faces anteriorly.

Posterior (dorsal): To the back of / behind eg. The scapula faces posteriorly.

Superior: Above eg. The head is superior to the neck.

Inferior: Below eg. The ankle is inferior to the knee.

Lateral: Away from the midline of the body eg. The shoulder lies lateral to the neck.

Medial: Towards the midline of the body eg. The big toe lies medial to the little toe.

Distal: Further away from the trunk / centre of the body eg. The foot is distal to the knee.

Proximal: Closer to the trunk / centre of the body eg. The hip is proximal to the knee.

Superficial: Closer to the surface of the skin

Deep: Further away from the surface of the skin (more into the bodies internal tissues).

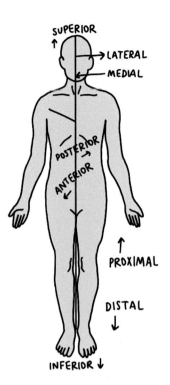

Figure 3. Illustration of the anatomical terms on the human body.

QUICK FIRE QUIZ! (Answers are at the back of this book!)

Fill in the blanks...

The elbow is................................. to the hand.

The hand is.................................... to the elbow.

The shoulder is................................ to the hand.

The nose sits................................ on the body.

Use these words to help you fill in the blanks, cross them off once you have used them!

Proximal   Superior   Anteriorly   Distal

MOVEMENT TERMS:

Now we have looked at the anatomical terms a little more closely, let us take a look at some terms used to describe different movements within the body.

Flexion: A movement that decreases the angle between 2 body parts e.g. bending the elbow is flexion as the angle between the forearm and the upper arm is decreased.

Extension: A movement that increases the angle between 2 body parts e.g. extending the elbow (straightening the arm) increases the angle between the forearm and the upper arm.

Plantarflexion: A movement where the tips of your toes point towards the ground (away from your leg).

Dorsiflexion: A movement where your toes point upwards towards the sky (away from the ground).

Abduction: Movement of a limb away from the midline of the body.

Adduction: Movement of a limb towards the midline of the body.

Medial rotation: A rotational movement of a limb towards the midline of the body e.g. bringing your towards your chest horizontally.

Lateral rotation: A rotational movement of a limb away from the midline of the body.

Supination: Rotation of the hand so that the palm faces forwards and upwards. In the foot, it usually means that the foot has rolled outwards which leaves an elevated arch, so the patient typically walks with more weight on the outside (lateral) edge of the foot.

Pronation: Rotation of the hand so that the palm faces downwards. In the foot, this typically means that there is more weight distributed on the inside edge (medial) of the foot. This is also typically seen with flat/ fallen arches.

Inversion: Movement of the foot in which the sole faces medially (it also consists of adduction and supination of the forefoot).

Eversion: Movement of the foot in which the sole of the foot faces laterally (it also consists of pronation and abduction of the forefoot).

MOVEMENT TERMS:

Here are a couple of movement related terms that will be useful to know!

AROM (Active range of motion): Active movement of joint (patient completes).

PROM (Passive range of motion): Light pressure applied to end feel of joint.

RROM (Resisted range of motion): Patient resists active movements.

End feel: The furthest physiological range a joint can be taken to.

QUICK FIRE QUIZ! (Answers are revealed at back of book!)

What is the movement in which a limb moves away from the midline of the body?

    A. Abduction
    B. Adduction

CHAPTER TWO

OVERVIEW OF COMPONENTS IN THE MUSCULOSKELETAL SYSTEM

SKELETON:

The bones of the human skeleton can be divided into 2 different groups. The appendicular skeleton and the axial skeleton. On this page we will take a look at both of these and see what bones are included within each.

THE AXIAL AND APPENDICULAR SKELETON:

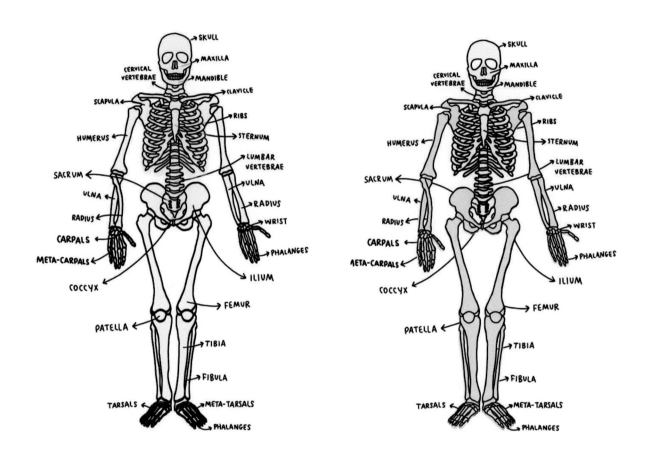

Figure 4. Illustrations of the axial (blue) and the appendicular (pink) skeletons.

AXIAL SKELETON: (The blue diagram shows the axial skeleton) The bones included in the axial skeleton are the frontal bone, maxilla, mandible, temporal bone, parietal bone, occipital bone, vertebral column, ribs, and the sternum.

APPENDICULAR SKELETON: (The pink diagram shows the appendicular skeleton) The bones included within the appendicular skeleton are the clavicle, scapula, humerus, ulna, radius, carpal bones, metacarpals, phalanges of hand, ilium, ischium, pubis, sacrum, coccyx, femur, patella, fibula, tarsal bones, metatarsals, and the phalanges of foot.

QUICK FIRE QUIZ!! (Answers at the back of book!)

Name 3 bones that are included within the axial skeleton.

1.   2.   3.

BONE STRUCTURE

Now we have covered the muscle structure, let us take a little look at the bone structure.

There are many different types of bones: short bones (e.g. Wrist bones), Long bones (e.g. Femur), Flat bones (e.g. Bones of skull), Irregular bones (eg. Vertebrae). The image below shows a dissected long bone, have a good look at this image!

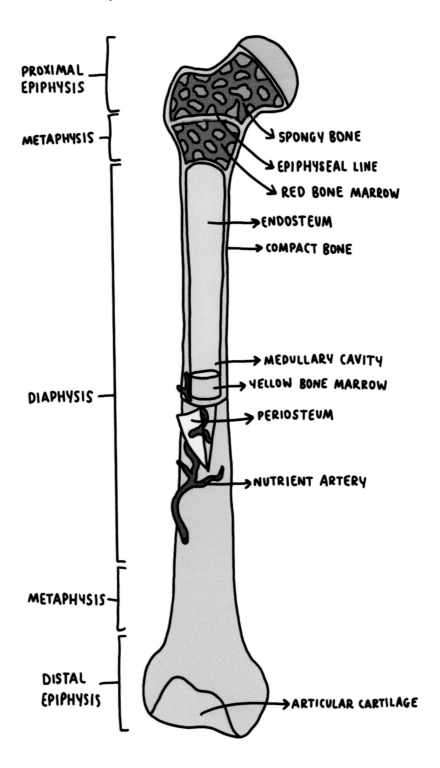

Figure 5. Illustration of a dissected bone (long bone)

QUICK FIRE QUIZ!! (Answers at the back of book!)

Name and explain some examples of different types of bone. (There are 4 different types!)

JOINTS

Now we have looked at both the bone and muscle structure, let us take a look at the different types of joints within the human body.

There are 3 different types of Joints:

- **Fibrous** (connected by dense connective tissue, they are also known as fixed joints, no movement eg. Skull bones)
- **Cartilaginous** (bones are entirely joined by cartilage, they have slightly more movement than the fibrous joints, however, have less movement than the synovial joints eg. Joints in between the vertebrae)
- **Synovial** (there is always a fluid filled capsule, and articular cartilage in these joints, a lot of movement can take place at these joints. This type of joint is the most common. Eg. Knee)

DIFFERENT TYPES OF SYNOVIAL JOINTS:

The synovial joint is the joint we will be focussing on within the guide. There are many different types of synovial joint. See the diagram below for more information.

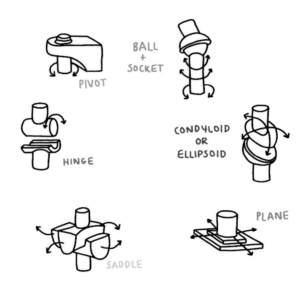

Figure 6. Illustration of the different types of synovial joints.

Pivot joint: Only allows movement around one single axis eg. Between C1 and C2 of vertebrae, allows rotation of neck.

Ball and socket joint: A joint where a ball shaped surface fits into a cup like surface. Movement is multiaxial. Eg. Shoulder.

Condyloid or ellipsoid joint: A joint where an ovoid surface fits into an elliptical cavity. This allows movement in 2 different planes. Eg. Joint between radius and carpal bones of the wrist.

Plane joint: Bones are able to slide over one another. Eg. In between tarsal bones.

Saddle joint: The reciprocating surfaces are usually concave and convex which means they can slide against one another. Eg. Thumb joint.

Hinge joint: A joint that allows movement in one direction and usually one plane (it works just like the hinge on a door!) eg. Elbow.

QUICK FIRE QUIZ!! (Answers at the back of book)

Name a type of synovial joint and give one example of this type of joint.

LEVERS

Having an understanding of how different levers work is crucial when working with forces being applied within the human body (such as during an injury). On this page we will be discussing the different types of levers, but first let us define what a lever actually is.

Lever: A lever is thought of as a rigid bar that is resting on a pivot.

Fulcrum: A fulcrum is the point in which a lever rotates (the pivot).

Now we have an understanding of a fulcrum and a lever let us take a look at the different classes of levers:

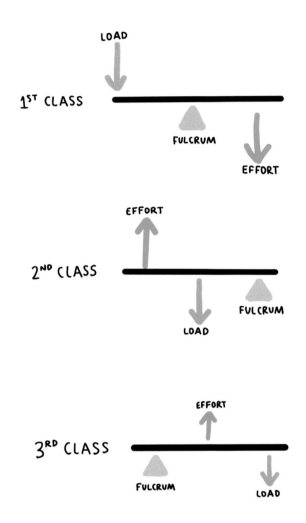

Figure 7. Illustration of the different classes of levers.

First class lever: The fulcrum is in the middle of the effort and load. This lever can be found in the neck when you look down or up.

Second class lever: The load is in the middle between the fulcrum and the effort. This lever can be found in the ankle area when you stand on tiptoes, can be used when jumping or pushing off.

Third class lever: The effort is in the middle between the fulcrum and the load. This lever is used during a biceps curl at the elbow joint.

QUICK FIRE QUIZ!! (Answers at back of book)

Name and explain an example of a second-class lever within the human body.

MUSCLE TISSUE

Now we have looked at the basic terms of reviewing human anatomy, let us take a closer look at the muscle tissues. There are 3 different types of muscle tissue within the human body.

Skeletal muscle: consists of long, cylindrical, striated fibres (striations- are variations in light and dark bands within the fibres which can be seen under a microscope). Skeletal muscles can vary in length, from a few centimetres up to 30-40cm. Skeletal muscle contractions are voluntary. Skeletal muscles are usually attached to the skeleton to form a part of the mechanical structure which allows the limbs to move freely. The function of these muscles is to aid motion, posture, heat production and provide general protection.

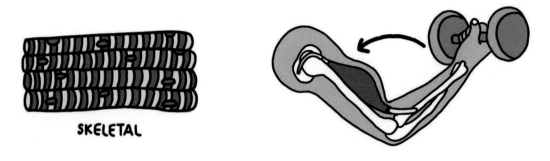

SKELETAL

Figure 8. Illustration of skeletal muscle fibres and an example of where they can be found, e.g. the biceps muscle.

Cardiac muscle: consists of branched, striated fibres. These are located within the heart wall (hence the name cardiac muscle!) The function of these muscles is to pump blood to the entire body.

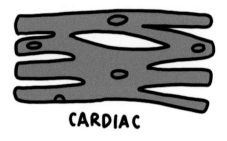

CARDIAC

Figure 9. Illustration of cardiac muscle fibres.

Smooth muscle: consists of nonstriated fibres (lack striations, so are smooth). These muscles can be found within various areas of the human body, such as the iris of the eyes, within blood vessels, airways such as the lungs, stomach, intestine, gallbladder, urinary bladder, and uterus. The function is to provide motion, e.g. constriction of blood vessels provides the flow of blood.

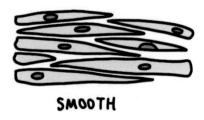

SMOOTH

Figure 10. Illustration of smooth muscle fibres.

QUICK FIRE QUIZ! (Answers at reverse of book!)

Are skeletal muscles striated? A. Yes B. No

MUSCLE ARRANGEMENTS

On this page, we shall take a look at the different muscle fibre arrangements within the human body. See the diagram below for more information about the different arrangements.

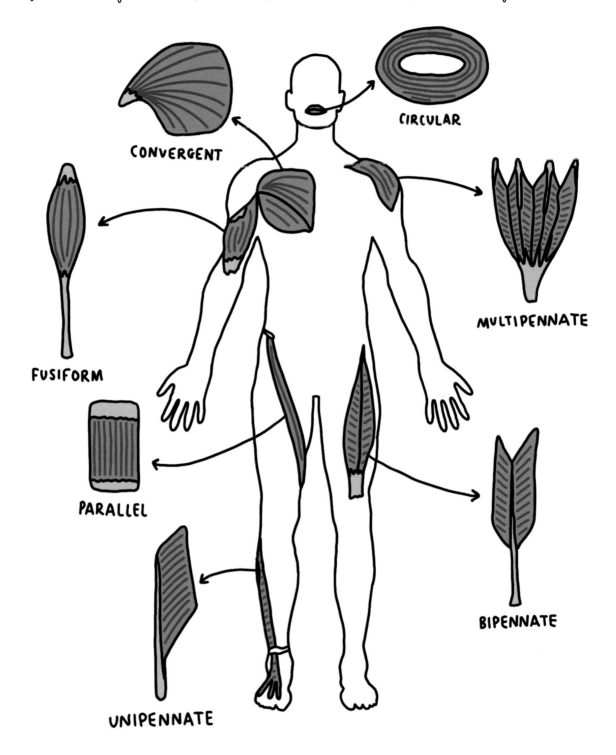

Figure 11. Illustration of the different muscle fibre arrangement types within the human body and where they are present.

QUICK FIRE QUIZ! (Answers are at the back of the book!)

Name 3 different types of muscle fibre arrangements...

1.   2.   3.

MUSCLE STRUCTURE OF SKELETAL MUSCLE TISSUE

So now we know the different types of muscle fibres and the different arrangements, let us take a closer look at the Skeletal muscle tissue, which is the type of tissue we will be mostly focussing on within this guide.

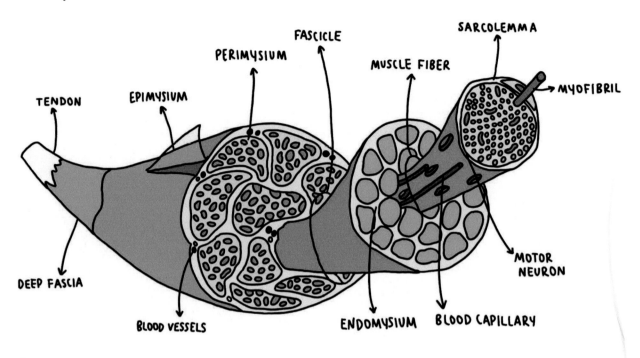

Figure 12. Illustration of a skeletal muscle fibre dissected. You can see the start of the muscle fibre (tendon), right down to the myofibril which sits centrally inside the muscle belly.

The image shown below, shows an individual muscle fibre which is made up of many myofibrils (shown in the diagram above). The individual fibre contains different zones which create different banding patterns on the outer side of the fibre. This creates the striation shown within the muscle. As a muscle contracts, the actin and myosin filaments overlap one another and create the interaction known as The Sliding Filament Theory, which will be discussed on the next page!

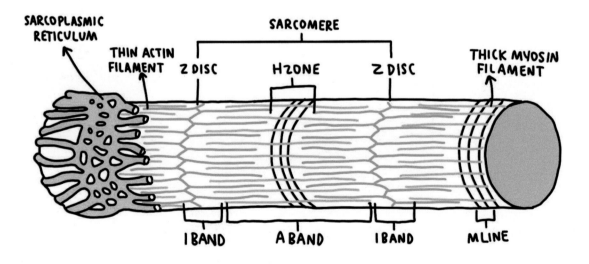

Figure 13. Illustration of an induvial muscle fibre which is composed of different bands.

QUICK FIRE QUIZ! (Answers shown at back of book!)

What is a muscle fibre made up of? Choose one answer!

A. Myosin   B. Myofibrils   C. Z Disk

CHAPTER THREE

THE PECTORAL GIRDLE

INRODUCTION TO THE UPPER LIMB AND PECTORAL GIRDLE

The shoulder blade (scapula) and clavicle are the bones of the pectoral girdle. We are going to take a closer look at the anatomical structures of each and identify the bony landmarks. Let us start by looking at the regions, bones, and joints of the upper arm.

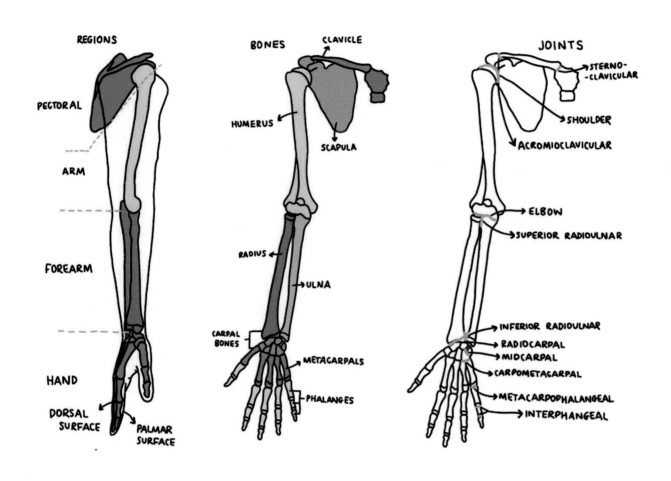

Figure 14. Illustration of the bones, regions, and joints of the upper limb.

Make sure to take a look over the diagram above and remember the different bones, regions, and different joints! It will really help you with understanding the individual structures in more detail. In this chapter we will be focussing more on the pectoral girdle area (scapula and clavicle) so make sure you are aware of where these bones lie and what joints are associated with this region of the body.

QUICK FIRE QUIZ! (Answers are at the back of this book!)

What bones are included within the pectoral girdle?

> A. Scapula and Clavicle
> B. Scapula and Phalanges
> C. Clavicle and Ulna
> D. Ulna and Radius

Here is another question that you might be able to work out... (extra marks if you do!)

What joints are included within the pectoral girdle?

> A. Acromioclavicular joint and Radiocarpal joint
> B. Sternoclavicular joint and Acromioclavicular joint
> C. Radiocarpal joint and Metacarpophalangeal joint
> D. Midcarpal joint and Sternoclavicular joint

BONES OF THE PECTORAL GIRDLE

Now you have been introduced to the bones, regions, and joints of the upper limb, let us take a closer look at the bony landmarks of the pectoral girdle bones—the scapula and clavicle.

THE SCAPULA:

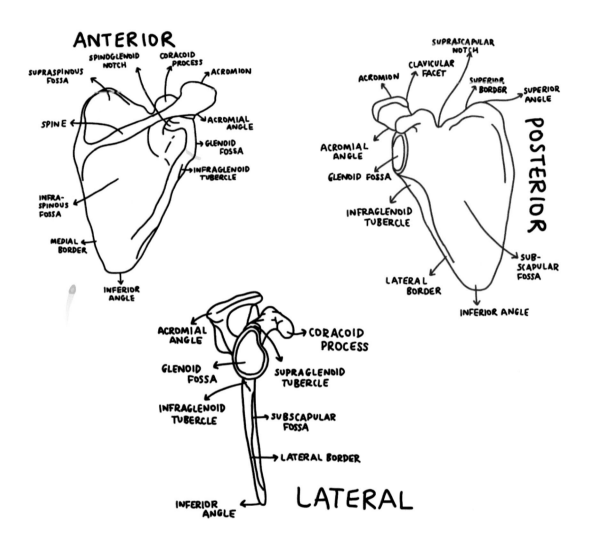

Figure 15. Illustration of the anterior, posterior, and lateral aspects of the scapula.

The key bony landmarks to take note of here, are the different borders of the scapula, such as the superior border etc. There are also important attachment sites shown here for crucial muscles that are vital for movements of the pectoral girdle and shoulder. The subscapular fossa is an example of an attachment site for the subscapularis muscle. See how the two relate? Subscapular- is used in both words, which makes it simpler to remember the attachment site! See whether you can find any other matching sections, it really does make learning anatomy much easier!

(Please note that not all the muscle attachment sites and the bony landmarks will match like this, it is just a tip for a few of them that might make it simpler to remember!)

QUICK FIRE QUIZ! (Answers are at the back of this book!)

What muscle attaches to the subscapular fossa? — Subscapular

BONES OF THE PECTORAL GIRDLE (CONTINUED)

So, now we have covered the scapula, we shall move onto the clavicle! See the images below for more details about the bony landmarks of the clavicle. The clavicle and scapula both work together to provide movement of the upper limb.

THE CLAVICLE:

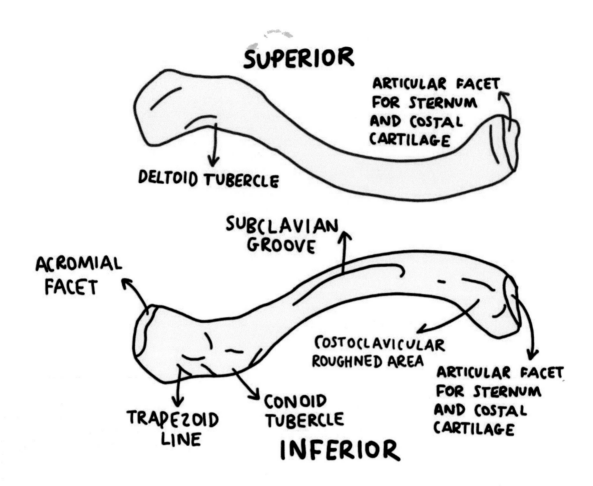

Figure 16. Illustration of the clavicle and the bony landmarks. This diagram shows the clavicle in both inferior and superior view.

The left side of the clavicle shown in this illustration is known as the acromial end, whilst the right side of this diagram is known as the sternal end. This highlights where the ends of the bone attach, eg. The sternal end attaches to the sternum in the chest.

QUICK FIRE QUIZ! (Answers at the end of this book!)

Where does the sternal end of the clavicle attach to?

A. Skull
B. First rib
C. Sternum
D. Mandible
E. Scapula

JOINTS OF THE PECTORAL GIRDLE

Now we have discussed the bones and bony landmarks, let us take some time to look at the joints of the pectoral girdle.

THE STERNOCLAVICULAR JOINT: (articulations between the sternum and the clavicle)

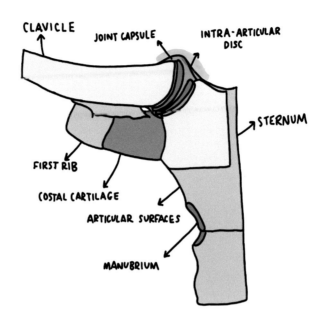

Figure 17. Illustration of the sternoclavicular joint.

TYPE OF JOINT	Synovial saddle joint; multiaxial
ARTICULAR SURFACES	Sternal end of clavicle, clavicular notch of sternum, superior surface of first costal cartilage; intra-articular fibrocartilaginous disc.
LIGAMENTS	Intrinsic ligaments: anterior and posterior sternoclavicular ligaments Extrinsic ligaments: interclavicular and costoclavicular ligaments
INNERVATION	Medial supraclavicular nerve, nerve to subclavius.
BLOOD SUPPLY	Suprascapular artery, internal thoracic artery.
MOVEMENTS	Elevation - depression Protraction - retraction Axial rotation

QUICK FIRE QUIZ! (Answers at the back of this book!)

Name a ligament involved within the sternoclavicular joint:

....

JOINTS OF THE PECTORAL GIRDLE (CONTINUED)

Now we have covered the sternoclavicular joint, let us take a look at the acromioclavicular joint which is the second joint of the pectoral girdle.

THE ACROMIOCLAVICULAR JOINT: (articulations between the acromion and the clavicle)

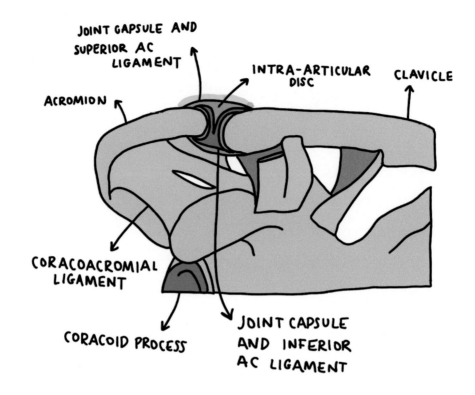

Figure 18. Illustration of the acromioclavicular joint.

TYPE OF JOINT	Synovial plane joint; multiaxial.
ARTICULAR SURFACES	Acromion of scapula, acromial end of clavicle.
LIGAMENTS	Intrinsic: Superior acromioclavicular ligament, inferior acromioclavicular ligament Extrinsic: Coracoclavicular ligament (with conoid and trapezoid parts)
INNERVATION	Lateral pectoral nerve, suprascapular nerve.
BLOOD SUPPLY	Thoracoacromial artery, suprascapular artery.
MOVEMENTS	Protraction – retraction Elevation – depression Axial rotation

QUICK FIRE QUIZ! (Answers at the back of book!)
Name a movement produced by the acromioclavicular joint.

LIGAMENTS OF THE PECTORAL GIRDLE

ANTERIOR STERNOCLAVICULAR LIGAMENT – Ligament that joins the sternum with the clavicle (anteriorly).

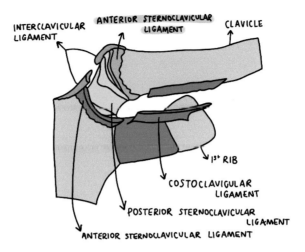

POSTERIOR STERNOCLAVICULAR LIGAMENT – Ligament that joins the sternum with the clavicle (posteriorly).

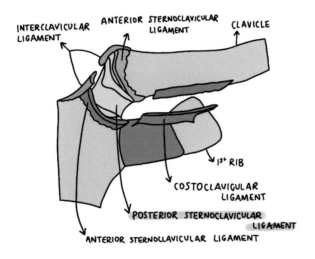

INTERCLAVICULAR LIGAMENT – Ligament that joins the sternal end of one clavicle to that of the other.

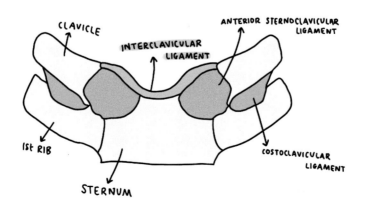

COSTOCLAVICULAR LIGAMENT- Ligament that joins the costal space between the first rib and the clavicle. This ligament helps to stabilise the Sternoclavicular joint.

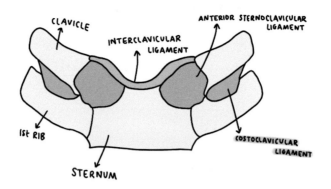

CORACOCLAVICULAR LIGAMENT- CONOID PART / TRAPEZOID PART- This ligament is made up of 2 parts. It joins the clavicle with the coracoid process of the scapula.

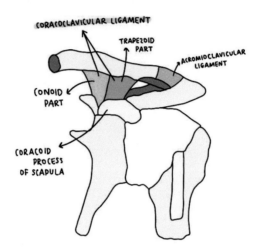

ACROMIOCLAVICULAR LIGAMENT (INFERIOR / SUPERIOR)- This ligament joins the acromion to the lateral end of the clavicle.

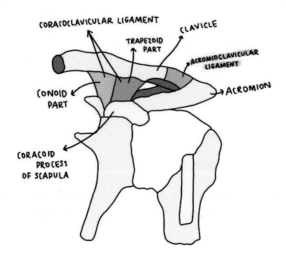

QUICK FIRE QUIZ! (Answers are at the back of this book!)

Name 3 ligaments that are found within the pectoral girdle.

1. 2.   3.

MUSCLES OF THE PECTORAL GIRDLE

Now we have looked over the bones, joints, and ligaments of the pectoral girdle, let us take a closer look at the muscles that enable the movements to take place.

MUSCLES RETRACTING THE PECTORAL (SHOULDER) GIRDLE:

RHOMBOID MINOR:

Origin: Nuchal ligament, Spinous processes of vertebrae C7-T1.

Insertion: Root (medial end) of spine of scapula.

Action: Scapulothoracic joint: Draws scapula superomedially, rotates glenoid cavity inferiorly; Supports position of scapula.

Innervation: Dorsal scapular nerve (C4-C5).

Blood supply: Dorsal scapular artery, deep branch of transverse cervical artery, dorsal branch of upper five or six posterior intercostal arteries.

RHOMBOID MAJOR:

Origin: Spinous process of vertebrae T2-T5.

Insertion: Medial border of scapula (from inferior angle to root of spine of scapula).

Action: Scapulothoracic joint: Draws scapula superomedially, rotates glenoid cavity inferiorly; Supports position of scapula.

Innervation: Dorsal scapular nerve (C4-C5).

Blood supply: Dorsal scapular artery, deep branch of transverse cervical artery, dorsal branch of upper five or six posterior intercostal arteries.

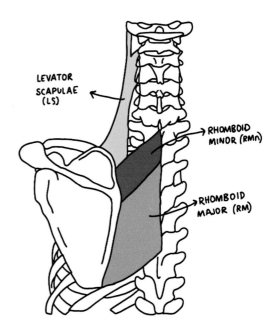

LEVATOR SCAPULAE (LS)

RHOMBOID MINOR (RMn)

RHOMBOID MAJOR (RM)

Figure 19. Illustration of the Rhomboid Minor and Rhomboid Major.

TRAPEZIUS (ALL FIBRES):

UPPER FIBRES:

Origin: Medial third of the superior nuchal line, external occipital protuberance.

Insertion: Lateral third of clavicle.

Action: Scapulothoracic joint: draws scapula superomedially. Atlantooccipital joint: extension of head and neck, lateral flexion of head and neck (ipsilateral). Atlantoaxial joint: rotation of head (contralateral).

Innervation: Motor: accessory nerve (CN XI). Motor/Sensory: ventral rami of spinal nerves C3-C4 (via cervical plexus).

Blood supply: Occipital artery (descending part), superficial or transverse cervical artery (transverse part), dorsal scapular artery (ascending part).

MIDDLE FIBRES:

Origin: Nuchal ligament attached to the spinous processes of C1–C6 vertebrae, spinous processes, and supraspinous ligaments of vertebrae C7–T3.

Insertion: Medial acromial margin, superior crest of spine of scapula.

Innervation: Motor: accessory nerve (CN XI) Motor/Sensory: ventral rami of spinal nerves C3–C4 (via cervical plexus)

Function: Scapulothoracic joint: draws scapula medially.

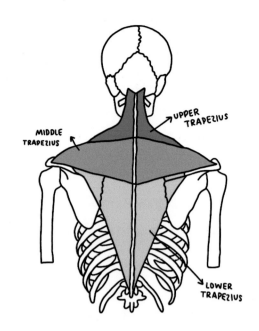

LOWER FIBRES:

Origin: Spinous processes and supraspinous ligaments of vertebrae T4–T12.

Insertion: Lateral apex of the medial end of scapular spine.

Innervation: Motor: accessory nerve (CN XI) Motor/Sensory: ventral rami of spinal nerves C3–C4 (via cervical plexus)

Function: Scapulothoracic joint: Draws scapula inferomedially.

MUSCLES PROTRACTING THE PECTORAL (SHOULDER) GIRDLE:

SERRATUS ANTERIOR:

Origin: Superior part: Ribs 1–2, Intercostal fascia, Middle part: Ribs-3–6, Inferior part: Ribs 7–8/9/10 (+ external oblique muscle).

Insertion: Superior part: Anterior and posterior surface of superior angle of scapula. Middle part: Anterior surface of entire medial border of scapula. Inferior part: Anterior and posterior surface of inferior angle of scapula.

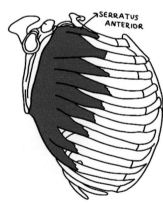

Innervation: Long thoracic nerve (C5– C7) (SALT Mnemonic)

Function: Scapulothoracic joint: Draws scapula anterolaterally, suspends scapula on thoracic wall, rotates scapula (draws inferiorly angle laterally).

PECTORALIS MINOR:

Origin: Anterior surface, costal cartilages of ribs 3-5.

Insertion: Medial border and coracoid process of scapula.

Innervation: Medial and lateral pectoral nerves (C5-T1).

Function: Scapulothoracic joint: draws scapula anteroinferiorly, stabilizes scapula on thoracic wall.

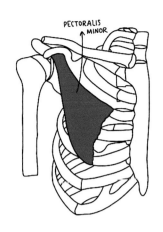

MUSCLES ELEVATING THE PECTORAL (SHOULDER) GIRDLE:

TRAPEZIUS (UPPER): See pages 33-34.

LEVATOR SCAPULAE:

Origin: Transverse processes of vertebrae C1-C4.

Insertion: Medial border of scapula (from superior angle to root of spine of scapula).

Innervation: Anterior rami of the nerves C3 and C4, dorsal scapular nerve (branch of the C5).

Function: Scapulothoracic joint: Draws scapula superomedially, rotates glenoid cavity inferiorly. Cervical joints: Lateral flexion of neck (ipsilateral), extension of the neck.

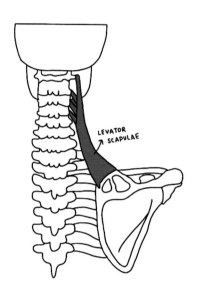

MUSCLES DEPRESSING THE PECTORAL (SHOULDER) GIRDLE:

TRAPEZIUS (LOWER FIBRES): See pages 33-34..

PECTORALIS MINOR: See page 35.

MUSCLES LATERALLY ROTATING THE PECTORAL (SHOULDER) GIRDLE:

TRAPEZIUS (ALL FIBRES): See pages 33-34.

SERRATUS ANTERIOR: See page 34.

MUSCLES MEDIALLY ROTATING THE PECTORAL (SHOULDER) GIRDLE:

RHOMBOID MAJOR: See page 33.

RHOMBOID MINOR: See page 33.

PECTORALIS MINOR: See page 35.

LEVATOR SCAPULAE: See page 35.

MUSCLES STABILIZING THE CLAVICLE:

SUBCLAVIUS:

Origin: Costal cartilage, sternal end of rib 1.

Insertion: Anteroinferior surface of middle third of clavicle.

Innervation: Subclavian nerve (C5-C6).

Blood supply: Clavicular branch of thoracoacromial artery, suprascapular artery.

Function: Sternoclavicular joint: Anchors and depresses clavicle.

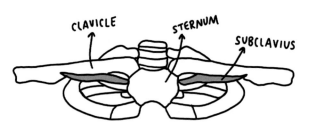

QUICK FIRE QUIZ! (Answers at the end of the book!)

What muscles medially rotate the pectoral girdle?

1.   2.   3.   4.

What is the action, origin, insertion, and innervation for the Trapezius upper fibres?

A: O: I: IN:

CHAPTER FOUR

THE SHOULDER

BONES OF THE SHOULDER

In this chapter we will be taking a closer look at the shoulder joint! On this page we will take a look at the bones involved within this joint.

First, we will be looking at the humerus bone in both anterior and posterior view:

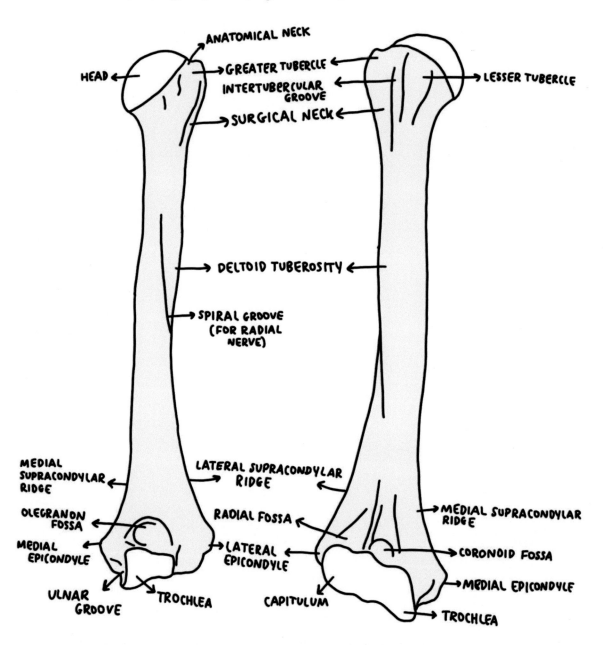

Figure 20. Illustration of the humerus bones (anteriorly and posteriorly).

In the diagram above we can see all of the bony landmarks of the humerus bone. Make sure you study this diagram closely and have a go at palpating these bony landmarks on yourself! Remember practice makes perfect!

QUICK FIRE QUIZ!! (Answers at the back of book!)

Name (and palpate if you can!) 2 bony landmarks on the humerus bone.

BONES OF THE SHOULDER

The other main bone involved within the shoulder joint is the scapula. We have previously looked at this bone during the first chapter on the pectoral girdle. Can you remember any of the bony landmarks of the scapula? Test yourself here, by filling in the missing labels on the diagram!

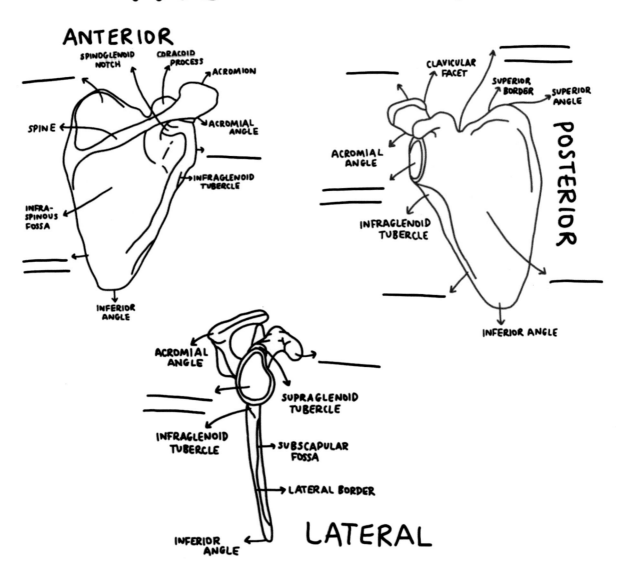

Figure 21. Illustration of the scapula in posterior, anterior and lateral view with blank labels.

How did you get on? You can check your answers at the back of this book! Do not worry if you did not get them all correct first time around! Go back to the pectoral girdle chapter and have another look at the diagram. Using flashcards or creating your own diagram is a really good way to practice and learn anatomy. You do not need to be an artist to draw these diagrams, just using simple circles and shapes can help you identify where the bony landmarks are!

QUICK QUIZ!! (Answers at the back of this book!)

Can you identify a bony landmark on the lateral side of the scapula?

THE SHOULDER JOINT

Now we have looked at the bones of the shoulder, let us take a closer look at all of the structures involved within the shoulder joint.

THE SHOULDER JOINT

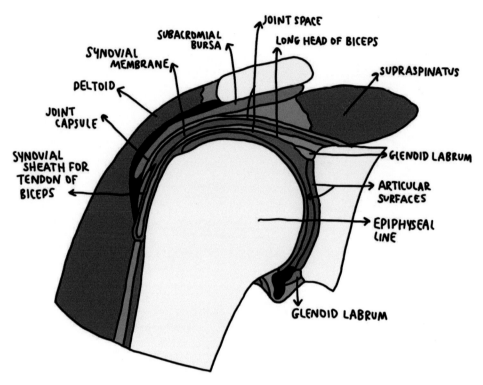

Figure 22. Illustration of the shoulder joint and structures involved within it.

TYPE OF JOINT	Synovial ball and socket joint; multiaxial.
ARTICULAR SURFACES	Glenoid fossa of scapula, head of humerus; glenoid labrum.
LIGAMENTS	Superior glenohumeral, middle glenohumeral, inferior glenohumeral, coracohumeral, transverse humeral.
INNERVATION	Subscapular nerve (joint); suprascapular nerve, axillary nerve, lateral pectoral nerve (joint capsule).
BLOOD SUPPLY	Anterior and posterior circumflex humeral, circumflex scapular and suprascapular arteries.
MOVEMENTS	Flexion, extension, abduction, adduction, external/lateral rotation, internal/medial rotation and circumduction.

QUICK QUIZ!! (Answers at the back of book!)

Name one of the ligaments involved in the shoulder joint.

LIGAMENTS OF THE SHOULDER JOINT

SUPERIOR GLENOHUMERAL LIGAMENT- This ligament joins the humerus to the glenoid superiorly.

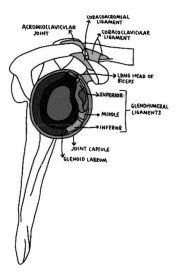

MIDDLE GLENOHUMERAL LIGAMENT- This ligament joins the humerus to the glenoid (in the middle).

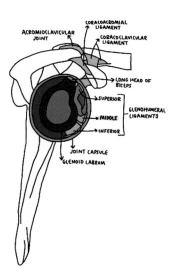

INFERIOR GLENOHUMERAL LIGAMENT- This ligament joins the humerus to the glenoid inferiorly.

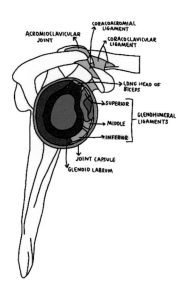

TRANSVERSE HUMERAL LIGAMENT- This ligament holds the long head of the biceps brachii in place on the humerus bone. It holds in between the greater and lesser tubercle.

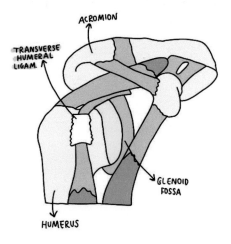

CORACOHUMERAL LIGAMENT- This ligament joins the coracoid process to the humerus bone.

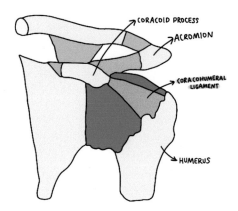

CORACOACROMIAL LIGAMENT- This ligament joins the conacoid process to the acromion.

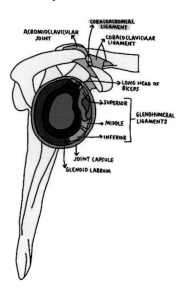

QUICK FIRE QUIZ!! (Answers at the back of book!)

What does the coracohumeral ligament join together?

MUSCLES OF THE SHOULDER JOINT

Now we have had a look at the shoulder joint in more detail, let us take a look at the muscles which help aid the movements at this joint.

MUSCLES ABDUCTING THE ARM AT THE SHOULDER JOINT:

SUPRASPINATUS:

Origin: Supraspinous fossa of scapula.

Insertion: Greater tubercle of humerus.

Innervation: Suprascapular nerve (C5,C6).

Function: Shoulder joint: Arm abduction; Stabilizes humeral head in glenoid cavity.

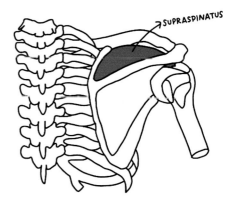

DELTOID:

Origin: Anterior part: Lateral third of clavicle. Middle part: Acromion of scapula. Posterior part: Spine of scapula.

Insertion: Deltoid tuberosity of humerus.

Innervation: Axillary nerve (C5, C6).

Blood supply: Deltoid and acromial branches of thoracoacromial artery, subscapular artery, anterior and posterior circumflex humeral arteries, deltoid branch of deep brachial artery.

Function: Anterior part: flexion and internal rotation of the arm. Middle part: abduction of the arm beyond the initial 15°. Posterior part: extension and external rotation of the arm.

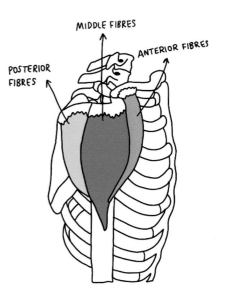

MUSCLES ADDUCTING THE ARM AT THE SHOULDER JOINT:

CORACOBRACHIALIS:

Origin: Coracoid process of the scapula.

Insertion: Anteromedial surface of the humerual shaft.

Action: Adduction and flexion of the arm at the shoulder joint.

Innervation: Musculocutaneous nerve (C5- C7).

Blood supply: Muscular branches of brachial artery.

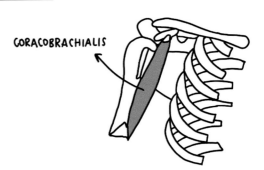

PECTORALIS MAJOR:

Origin: Clavicular part: anterior surface of medial half of clavicle. Sternocostal part: anterior surface of sternum, Costal cartilages of ribs 1-6.

Insertion: Crest of greater tubercle of humerus.

Innervation: Lateral and medial pectoral nerves (C5-T1).

Function: Shoulder joint: Arm adduction, Arm internal rotation, Arm flexion (clavicular head), arm extension (sternocostal head); Scapulothoracic joint: Draws scapula anteroinferiorly.

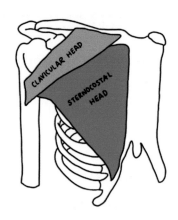

LATISSIMUS DORSI:

Origin: Vertebral part: Spinous processes of vertebrae T7-T12, Thoracolumbar fascia. Iliac part: Posterior third of crest of ilium. Costal part: Ribs 9-12. Scapular part: Inferior angle of scapula.

Insertion: Intertubercular sulcus of the humerus, between pectoralis major and teres major muscles.

Innervation: Thoracodorsal nerve (C6-C8).

Blood supply: Thoracodorsal artery, perforating arteries of the 9th-11th posterior intercostal arteries, and 1st-3rd lumbar arteries.

Functions: Shoulder joint: Arm internal rotation, Arm adduction, Arm extension; Assists in respiration.

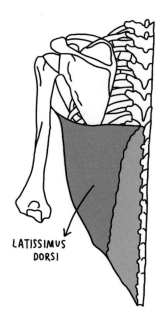

LATISSIMUS DORSI

TERES MAJOR:

Origin: Inferior angle and lower part of the lateral border of the scapula.

Insertion: Intertubercular sulcus (medial lip) of the humerus.

Innervation: Lower subscapular nerve (C5-C7).

Blood supply: Thoracodorsal branch of subscapular artery and posterior circumflex humeral artery.

Function: Extension and internal rotation of the humerus (arm).

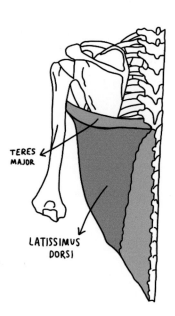

TERES MAJOR

LATISSIMUS DORSI

MUSCLES FLEXING THE ARM AT THE SHOULDER JOINT:

PECTORALIS MAJOR: See page 44.

DELTOID (ANTERIOR FIBRES): See page 43.

BICEPS BRACHII (LONG HEAD):

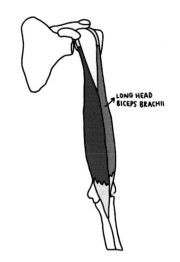

LONG HEAD
BICEPS BRACHII

Origin : Long head - Supraglenoid tubercle of the scapula.

Insertion: Radial tuberosity of the radius. Deep fascia of forearm (insertion of the bicipital aponeurosis).

Innervation: Musculocutaneous nerve (C5- C6).

Blood supply: Branches of brachial artery.

Function: Flexion and supination of the forearm at the elbow joint, weak flexor of the arm at the glenohumeral joint.

CORACOBRACHIALIS: See page 43.

MUSCLES EXTENDING THE ARM AT THE SHOULDER JOINT:

LATISSIMUS DORSI: See page 44.

TERES MAJOR: See page 44.

PECTORALIS MAJOR: See page 44.

DELTOID (POSTERIOR FIBRES): See page 43.

TRICEPS (LONG HEAD):

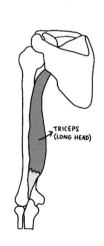

TRICEPS
(LONG HEAD)

Origins: Long head - infraglenoid tubercle of the scapula.

Insertion: Olecranon of ulna and fascia of forearm.

Action: Elbow joint: extension of the forearm. Shoulder joint: extension and adduction of the arm (long head).

Innervation: Radial nerve (C6-C8).

Blood supply: Deep brachial artery, superior ulnar collateral artery.

MUSCLES MEDIALLY ROTATING THE ARM AT THE SHOULDER JOINT:

SUBSCAPULARIS:

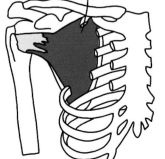

SUBSCAPULARIS

Origin: Subscapular fossa of scapula.

Insertion: Lesser tubercle of humerus.

Action : Shoulder joint: Arm internal rotation. Stabilizes humeral head in glenoid cavity.

Innervation: Upper and lower subscapular nerves (C5 - C6).

Blood supply: Suprascapular artery, axillary artery, subscapular artery.

TERES MAJOR: See page 44.

LATISSIMUS DORSI: See page 44.

PECTORALIS MAJOR: See page 44.

DELTOID (ANTERIOR FIBRES): See page 43.

MUSCLES LATERALLY ROTATING THE ARM AT THE SHOULDER JOINT:

TERES MINOR:

Origin: Lateral border of scapula.

Insertion: Greater tubercle of humerus.

Action: Shoulder joint: Arm external rotation, arm adduction; Stabilizes humeral head in glenoid cavity.

Innervation: Axillary nerve (C5, C6).

Blood supply: Suprascapular artery, dorsal scapular artery.

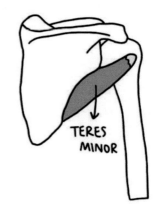

INFRASPINATUS:

Origin: Infraspinous fossa of scapula.

Insertion: Greater tubercle of humerus.

Action: Shoulder joint: Arm external rotation; Stabilizes humeral head in glenoid cavity

Innervation: Suprascapular nerve (C5, C6).

Blood supply: Suprascapular artery, circumflex scapular arteries.

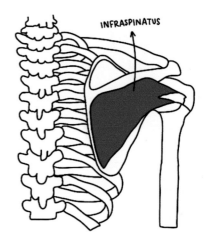

DELTOID (POSTERIOR FIBRES): See page 43.

QUIZ FIRE QUIZ!! (Answers at the back of book!)

Name 2 muscles that medially rotate the shoulder joint.

1.   2.

CHAPTER FIVE

THE ELBOW

BONES OF THE ELBOW

Now we have covered all of the pectoral girdle and the shoulder joint, we will be looking at the elbow joint in more detail! The following pages will be focussing on the bones of the elbow. Below is a diagram of the ulna and radius bones of the forearm which help to articulate the elbow joint.

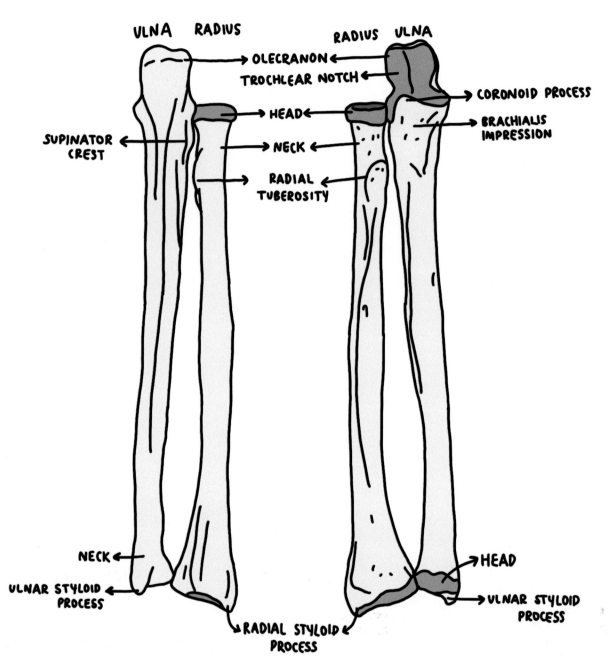

Figure 23. Illustration of the ulna and radius bones of the forearm in both an anterior and posterior view.

QUICK FIRE QUIZ!! (Answers at the back of this book!)

Name the 2 bones that are present in the forearm.

1.   2.

What side does the ulna face when the forearm is supinated? (Palm up)

· ·

BONES OF THE ELBOW (CONTINUED)

The humerus bone also makes up a part of the elbow joint. The humerus articulates with the ulna and radius to create the elbow joint. Now since we already discussed the humerus in the shoulder chapter, let us have another go at filling in the missing gaps! If you need to take a re-fresher head over to (enter page no.) to get a re-cap. Then get filling in!

THE HUMERUS

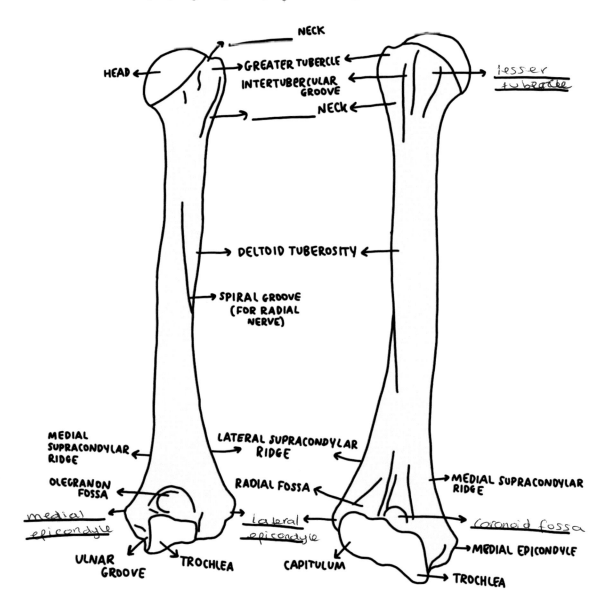

Figure 24. Illustration with missing gaps of the humerus bone.

QUICK FIRE QUIZ!! (Answers at the back of this book!)

Can you name the bones (there are 2!) that articulate with the humerus to create the elbow joint?

1.   2.

THE ELBOW JOINT

Now we have taken a look at the bones of the elbow joint, let us take a closer look at the different structures that make up the elbow joint.

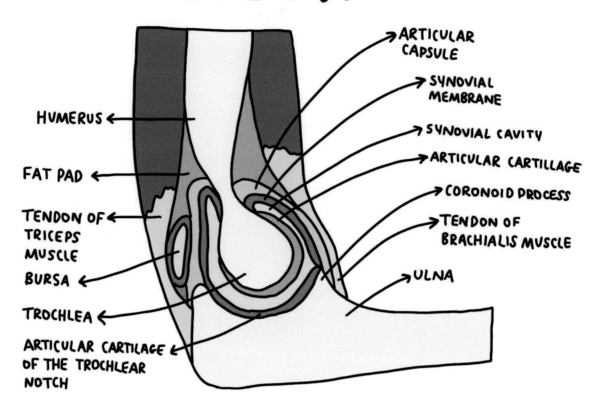

Figure 25. Illustration of the elbow joint in a sagittal section through the right elbow.

TYPE	Hinge joint.
BONES	Humerus, radius, ulna.
LIGAMENTS	Ulnar collateral ligament, radial collateral ligament, annular ligament, quadrate ligament.
BLOOD SUPPLY	Proximal to elbow joint - Ulnar collateral artery, radial collateral artery, middle collateral artery. Distal to elbow joint - Radial recurrent artery, ulnar recurret artery.
MOVEMENTS	Flexion - Biceps brachii, Brachialis, Brachioradialis muscles Extension - Triceps brachii muscle.

QUICK FIRE QUIZ!! (Answers at the end of this book!)

What movements are produced at the elbow joint?

1.   2.

50

LIGAMENTS OF THE ELBOW JOINT

ULNAR COLLATERAL LIGAMENT: This ligament connects the humerus to the ulna medially (on the inside of the elbow).

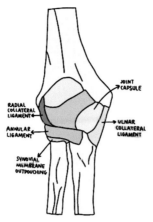

RADIAL COLLATERAL LIGAMENT: This ligament connects the humerus to the radius bone laterally (on the outside of the elbow).

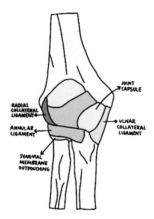

ANNULAR LIGAMENT: This ligament encircles the head of the radius and is attached to the ulna; this allows the head of the radius to be kept by the head of the ulna for smoother articulation with the humerus bone.

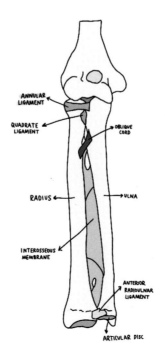

QUADRATE LIGAMENT: This ligament runs from the inferior border of the annular ligament to the neck of the radius.

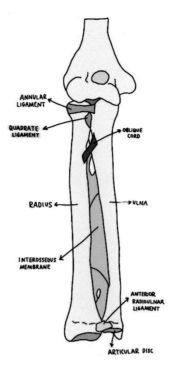

QUICK FIRE QUIZ!! (Answers are at the back of this book!)

Name and explain the location of 2 ligaments found within the elbow joint.

1.   Location:

2.   Location:

MUSCLES OF THE ELBOW JOINT

Now we have looked at the different structures involved within the elbow joint, let us take some time to look a little more closely at the muscles that enable the elbow joint to move.

MUSCLES FLEXING THE ELBOW JOINT:

BICEPS BRACHII:

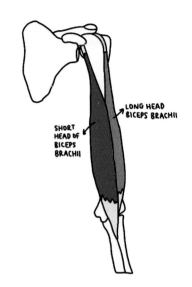

Origin: Short head – Apex of the Coracoid process of the scapula. Long head – Supraglenoid tubercle of the scapula.

Insertion: Radial tuberosity of the radius. Deep fascia of forearm (insertion of the bicipital aponeurosis).

Innervation: Musculocutaneous nerve ((5- (6).

Blood supply: Branches of brachial artery.

Function: Flexion and supination of the forearm at the elbow joint, weak flexor of the arm at the glenohumeral joint.

BRACHIALIS:

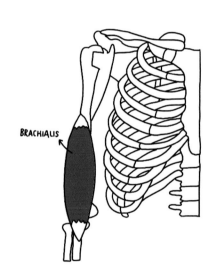

Origin: Distal half of anterior surface of humerus.

Insertion: Coronoid process of the ulna; Tuberosity of ulna.

Innervation: Musculocutaneous nerve ((5,(6); Radial nerve ((7).

Blood supply: Brachial artery, radial recurrent artery, (occasionally) branches from the superior and inferior ulnar collateral arteries.

Functions: Strong flexion of forearm at the elbow joint.

BRACHIORADIALIS:

Origin: Lateral supracondylar ridge of humerus, lateral intermuscular septum of arm.

Insertion: (Proximal to) styloid process of radius.

Action: Elbow joint- Forearm flexion (when semi pronated).

Innervation: Radial nerve (C5-C6).

Blood supply: Radial artery, radial recurrent arteries, radial collateral artery.

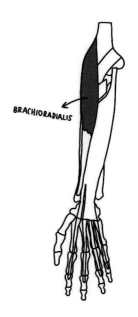

PRONATOR TERES:

Origin: Humeral head: medial supracondylar ridge of humerus. Ulnar head: Coronoid process of ulna.

Insertion: Lateral surface of radius (distal to supinator).

Action: Pronation of forearm at the proximal radioulnar joint, flexion of the forearm at the elbow joint.

Innervation: Median nerve (C6, C7).

Blood supply: Branches of brachial, radial and ulnar arteries.

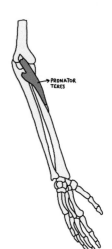

MUSCLES EXTENDING THE ELBOW JOINT:

TRICEPS BRACHII:

Origins: Long head - infraglenoid tubercle of the scapula. Medial head - posterior surface of the humerus (inferior to radial groove). Lateral head - posterior surface of the humerus (superior to radial groove).

Insertion: Olecranon of ulna and fascia of forearm.

Action: Elbow joint- extension of the forearm. Shoulder joint: extension and adduction of the arm (long head).

Innervation: Radial nerve (C6-C8).

Blood supply: Deep brachial artery, superior ulnar collateral artery.

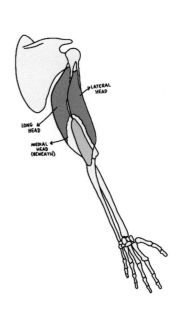

ANCONEUS:

Origin: Lateral epicondyle of humerus.

Insertion: Lateral surface of olecranon.

Action : Assists in forearm extension at the elbow joint; Stabilization of elbow joint.

Innervation: Radial nerve (C7-C8).

Blood supply: Posterior interosseous recurrent artery.

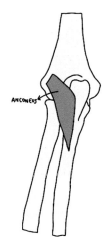

QUICK FIRE QUIZ!! (Answers at the back of the book!)

What is the action of the brachialis muscle?

Action: ....

CHAPTER SIX

THE FOREARM

BONES OF THE FOREARM

On this page we will discuss the bones of the forearm. Now, we have already previously discussed these over on (enter page no.) during the chapter on the elbow. Can you remember much about these bones? I have left a few gaps for you to try and fill in! See what you can recall... (note, this is a slightly different diagram used from the pages mentioned- however this diagram is still shown in the chapter on the elbow!)

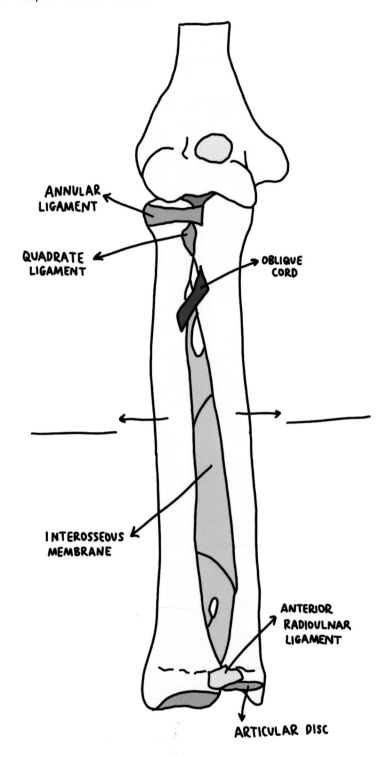

ANNULAR
LIGAMENT

QUADRATE
LIGAMENT

OBLIQUE
CORD

INTEROSSEOUS
MEMBRANE

ANTERIOR
RADIOULNAR
LIGAMENT

ARTICULAR DISC

Figure 26. Illustration of the forearm bones, including the interosseous membrane.

QUICK FIRE QUIZ!!

What does the annular ligament do?

....

JOINTS OF THE FOREARM

Now we have had a look at the bones of the forearm, let us take a little look at the joints. There are 2 different joints. The superior radioulnar joint, and the inferior radioulnar joint.

THE SUPERIOR RADIOULNAR JOINT:

Type	Synovial pivot joint; uniaxial.
Articular surfaces	Head of radius, radial fossa of ulna.
Ligaments	Annular ligament, quadrate ligament.
Innervation	Median, musculocutaneous, radial and ulnar nerves.
Blood supply	Deep brachial, radial and common interosseous arteries.
Movements	Pronation — supination.

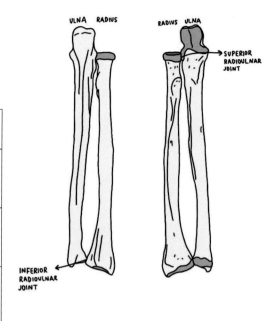

Figure 27. Illustration of the radius and ulnar showing the 2 different joints of the forearm (the superior radioulnar joint, and the inferior radioulnar joint).

THE INFERIOR RADIOULNAR JOINT:

Type	Synovial pivot joint; uniaxial.
Articular surfaces	Distal head of ulna, ulnar notch of radius.
Ligaments	Triangular fibrocartilage complex: Articular disc of distal radioulnar joint, ulnar collateral ligament, dorsal and palmar radioulnar ligaments, base of extensor carpi ulnaris sheath, ulnolunate and ulnotriquetral ligaments.
Innervation	Anterior and posterior interosseous nerves.
Blood supply	Anterior interosseous, posterior interosseous and ulnar arteries.
Movements	Pronation — supination.

QUICK FIRE QUIZ!! (Answers at the back of this book!)

What is the blood supply of the inferior radioulnar joint?

LIGAMENTS OF THE FOREARM

ANNULAR LIGAMENT: See page 51.

QUADRATE LIGAMENT: See page 52.

TRIANGULAR FIBROCARTILLAGE COMPLEX: This is a load bearing structure which is situated between the lunate, triquetrum and ulnar head. It acts as a stabilizer for the ulnar aspect of the wrist.

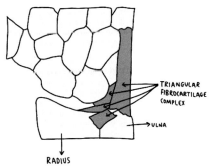

QUICK FIRE QUIZ!! (Answers at the back of book!)

What does the triangular fibrocartilage complex act as?

....

MUSCLES OF THE FOREARM

Now we have looked at the joints, the bones and the ligaments of the forearm, let us take a look at the muscles.

MUSCLES SUPINATING THE FOREARM:

SUPINATOR:

Origin: Lateral epicondyle of humerus, radial collateral ligament, annular ligament, supinator crest of ulna.

Insertion: Lateral, posterior, and anterior surfaces of proximal third of radius.

Action: Proximal radioulnar joint- Forearm supination.

Innervation: Posterior interosseous nerve (C7, C8).

Blood supply: Radial recurrent artery, posterior interosseous artery, posterior interosseous recurrent artery.

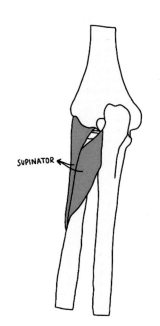

BICEPS BRACHII: See page 53.

BRACHIORADIALIS: See page 54.

MUSCLES PRONATING THE FOREARM:

PRONTATOR TERES: See page 54.

PRONATOR QUADRATUS:

Origins: Distal anterior surface of ulna.

Insertion: Distal anterior surface of radius.

Actions: Proximal radioulnar joint: Forearm pronation.

Innervation: Median nerve (anterior interosseous nerve, C7, C8).

Blood supply: Anterior interosseous artery.

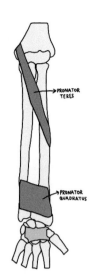

BRACHIORADIALIS: See page 54.

QUICK FIRE QUIZ!! (Answers at the back of book!)

Name 2 of the muscles that are supinators of the forearm.

    1.   2.

Name 2 of the muscles that are pronators of the forearm.

    1.   2.

CHAPTER
SEVEN
THE WRIST

BONES OF THE WRIST

On this page we will be looking at the bones that make up the wrist joint. The radius and ulna both make up a part of the wrist joint, however, we have already looked at both of these bones in both the elbow and forearm chapters. Check out pages (enter no.) for more information on these.

The other bones involved within the wrist joint are the carpus bones. The carpus consists of 8 separate bones. The 8 bones include, the scaphoid, the lunate, the triquetral, the pisiform, the trapezium, the trapezoid, the capitate, and the hamate. See the diagram below for more information on each of the locations.

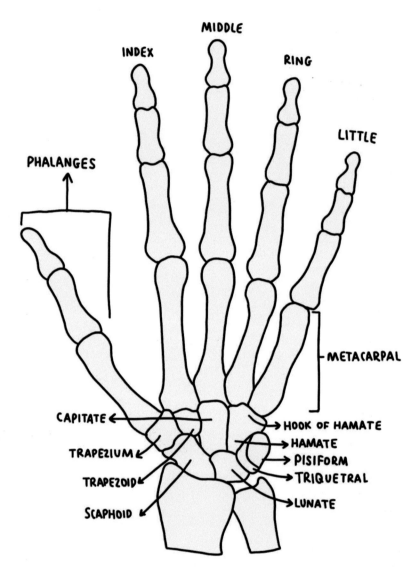

Figure 28. Illustration of the bones of the wrist (the carpus).

QUICK FIRE QUIZ!! (Answers at the back!)

Can you name the 8 bones which make up the carpus?

1.   2.   3.

4.   5.   6.

7.   8.

JOINTS OF THE WRIST

On this page we will be looking at the joints of the wrist, including the radiocarpal joints, the intercarpal joint, and the midcarpal joint.

THE RADIOCARPAL JOINT:

Type	Synovial ellipsoid joint;
Articular surfaces	Proximal component - distal end of radius, articular disc Distal component - scaphoid, lunate and triquetral of the proximal row of carpal bones (also includes triangular fibrocartilage complex)
Ligaments	Palmar radiocarpal joint, dorsal radiocarpal ligament, ulnar collateral ligament, radial collateral ligament
Innervation	Anterior interosseous nerve arising from median nerve (C5-T1) Posterior interosseous nerve arising from radial nerve (C7-C8) Deep and dorsal branches of the ulnar nerve (C8-T1)
Blood supply	Branches of the dorsal and palmar carpal arches
Movements	Flexion, extension, adduction and abduction

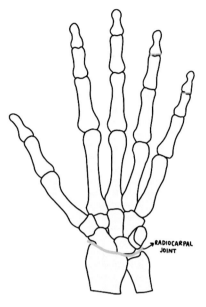

Figure 29. Illustration of the radiocarpal joint.

Figure 30. Illustration of the intercarpal joints.

THE INTERCARPAL JOINTS:

Type	Synovial plane joints; biaxial
Articular surfaces	Joints of the proximal carpal row: Adjacent articular surfaces of scaphoid, lunate, and triquetrum bones Joints of the distal carpal row: Adjacent articular surfaces of trapezium, trapezoid, capitate and hamate bones Midcarpal joint: distal articular surfaces of proximal carpal bones, proximal articular surfaces of distal carpal bones
Ligaments	Interosseous ligaments of proximal and distal carpal rows, palmar intercarpal, dorsal intercarpal ligaments

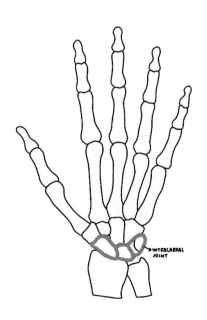

61

Innervation	Articular branches of anterior interosseous nerve, posterior interosseous nerve, deep and dorsal branches of ulnar nerve
Blood supply	Palmar and dorsal carpal arches
Movements	Flexion-extension, abduction-adduction, circumduction

THE MIDCARPAL JOINTS:

Articulations	Articulation between the proximal and distal row of carpal bones.
Joint capsule	Synovial gliding joints
Ligaments	Intercarpal, palmar intercarpal, dorsal intercarpal, radial collateral, ulnar collateral ligaments

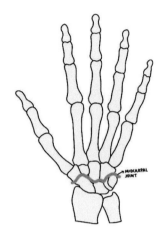

Figure 31. Illustration of the midcarpal joints.

QUICK FIRE QUIZ!! (Answers at the back of book!)

What movements are created from the intercarpal joints?

LIGAMENTS OF THE WRIST

PALMAR RADIOCARPAL LIGAMENT: A ligament that attaches to the radius, and connects to the styloid process, and the front and lower end of the ulna.

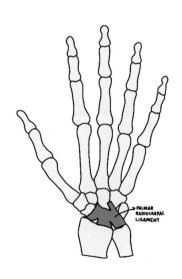

DORSAL RADIOCARPAL LIGAMENT: A ligament that connects the radius bone to the lunate and triquetral bone.

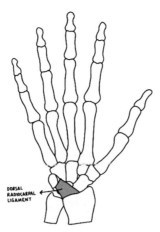

PALMAR ULNOCARPAL LIGAMENT: A ligament that runs from the base of the ulnar styloid process to the anterior surfaces of the carpal bones.

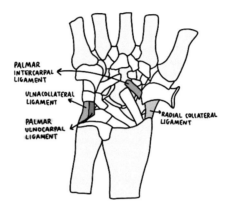

ULNAR COLLATERAL LIGAMENT: A ligament that is attached to the end of the styloid process of the ulna to the triquetrum and the pisiform bone.

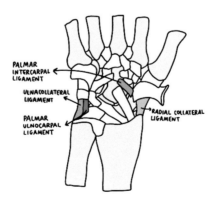

RADIAL COLLATERAL LIGAMENT: A ligament that runs from the radius to the scaphoid bone and the trapezium.

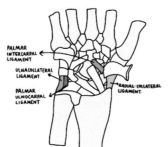

INTEROSSEOUS LIGAMENT: A ligament that runs from the lateral side of the capitate to the scaphoid near the trapezoid articular surface.

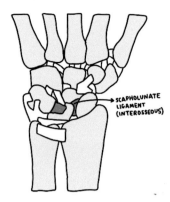

PALMAR INTERCARPAL LIGAMENT: These are fibrous bands that joins the palmar surfaces of the carpal bones together adjacently.

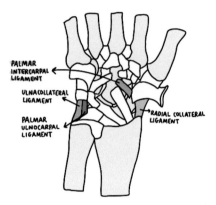

DORSAL INTERCARPAL LIGAMENT: These are also a fibrous band that joins the dorsal surfaces of the carpal bones together adjacently.

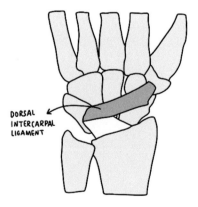

QUICK FIRE QUIZ!! (Answers at the back of this book!)

Name one ligament involved in the movements of the wrist.

....

MUSCLES OF THE WRIST

Now we have looked at the ligaments of the wrist. Let us take a look at the muscles involved in the movement of the wrist.

MUSCLES FLEXING THE WRIST:

FLEXOR CARPI ULNARIS:

Origin: Medial epicondyle of humerus, olecranon and posterior border of ulna.

Insertion: Pisiform bone, hamate bone, base of metacarpal bone 5.

Action: Wrist joint- Wrist flexion, wrist adduction.

Innervation: Ulnar nerve (C7-T1).

Blood Supply: Posterior ulnar recurrent artery, ulnar artery.

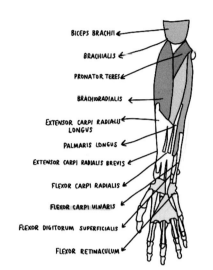

FLEXOR CARPI RADIALIS:

Origin: Medial epicondyle of humerus.

Insertion: Bases of metacarpal bones 2-3.

Action : Wrist joint- Wrist flexion, wrist abduction.

Innervation: Median nerve (C6, C7).

Blood supply: Anterior/posterior recurrent ulnar artery, radial artery.

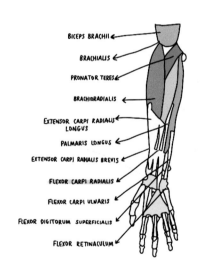

PALMARIS LONGUS:

Origin: Medial epicondyle of humerus.

Insertion: Flexor retinaculum, palmar aponeurosis.

Action: Wrist joint- Wrist flexion; Tenses palmar aponeurosis.

Innervation: Median nerve (C7, C8).

Blood supply: Anterior ulnar recurrent artery, median artery.

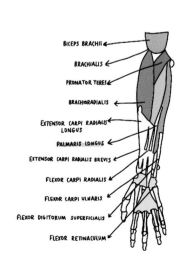

FLEXOR DIGITORUM SUPERFICILAIS:

Origin: Humeroulnar head: Medial epicondyle of humerus, coronoid process of ulna. Radial head: Proximal half of anterior border of radius.

Insertion: Sides of middle phalanges of digits 2-5.

Action: Metacarpophalangeal and proximal interphalangeal joints 2-5: Finger flexion.

Innervation: Median nerve (C8, T1).

Blood supply: Ulnar artery, radial artery, median artery.

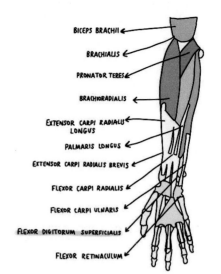

BICEPS BRACHII
BRACHIALIS
PRONATOR TERES
BRACHIORADIALIS
EXTENSOR CARPI RADIALIS LONGUS
PALMARIS LONGUS
EXTENSOR CARPI RADIALIS BREVIS
FLEXOR CARPI RADIALIS
FLEXOR CARPI ULNARIS
FLEXOR DIGITORUM SUPERFICIALIS
FLEXOR RETINACULUM

FLEXOR DIGITORUM PROFUNDUS:

Origin: Proximal half of anterior surface of ulna, interosseous membrane.

Insertion: Palmar surfaces of distal phalanges of digits 2-5.

Action : Metacarpophalangeal and interphalangeal joints 2-5: Finger flexion.

Innervation: Digits 2-3: Median nerve (anterior interosseous nerve); Digits 4-5: Ulnar nerve (C8, T1).

Blood supply: Ulnar, common interosseous, ulnar collateral, ulnar recurrent, anterior interosseous, median arteries.

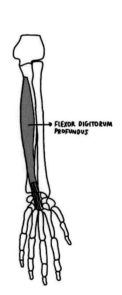

FLEXOR DIGITORUM PROFUNDUS

FLEXOR POLLICIS LONGUS:

Origin: Anterior surface of radius and interosseous membrane.

Insertion: Palmar surface of distal phalanx of thumb.

Action: Metacarpophalangeal and interphalangeal joint 1; Thumb flexion.

Innervation: Median nerve (anterior interosseous nerve (C7, C8).

Blood supply: Medial part: anterior interosseous artery (ulnar artery); lateral part: radial artery.

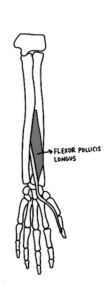

FLEXOR POLLICIS LONGUS

MUSCLES EXTENDING THE WRIST:

EXTENSOR CARPI RADIALIS LONGUS:

Origin: Lateral supracondylar ridge of humerus, lateral intermuscular septum of arm.

Insertion: Posterior aspect of base of metacarpal bone 2.

Actions: Wrist joints: Hand extension, hand abduction (radial deviation).

Innervation: Radial nerve ((C5-C8).

Blood supply: Radial recurrent artery, radial collateral artery, radial artery.

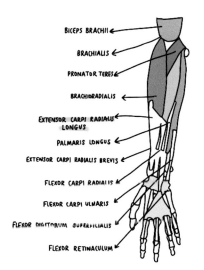

EXTENSOR CARPI RADIALIS BREVIS:

Origin: Lateral epicondyle of humerus (common extensor tendon).

Insertion: Posterior aspect of base of metacarpal bone 3.

Action : Wrist joints: Hand extension, hand abduction (radial deviation).

Innervation: Radial nerve ((C5- C6).

Blood supply: Radial recurrent artery, radial artery, deep brachial artery.

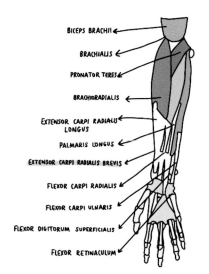

EXTENSOR CARPI ULNARIS:

Origin: Lateral epicondyle of humerus, posterior border of ulna.

Insertion: Base of metacarpal bone 5.

Action : Wrist joint: Hand extension and adduction.

Innervation: Posterior interosseous nerve ((C7, C8).

Blood supply: Radial recurrent artery, posterior interosseous artery.

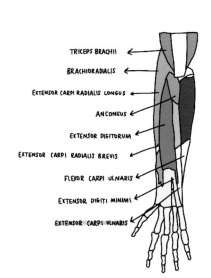

EXTENSOR DIGITORUM:

Origin: Lateral epicondyle of humerus (common extensor tendon).

Insertion: Extensor expansions of digits 2-5.

Action: Metacarpophalangeal / Interphalangeal joints 2-5: Finger extension.

Innervation: Posterior interosseous nerve (C7, C8).

Blood supply: Posterior interosseous artery, radial recurrent artery, anterior interosseous artery.

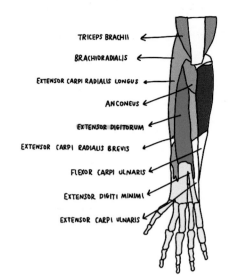

EXTENSOR INDICIS:

Origin: Posterior surface of distal third of ulna and interosseus membrane.

Insertion: Extensor expansion of index finger.

Action: Wrist joints: Weak hand extension. Metacarpophalangeal and interphalangeal joints of index finger: Finger extension.

Innervation: Posterior interosseous nerve (C7, C8).

Blood supply: Posterior and anterior interosseous artery.

EXTENSOR DIGITI MINIMI:

Origin: Lateral epicondyle of humerus (common extensor tendon).

Insertion: Extensor expansion of digit 5.

Action: Metacarpophalangeal joint 5: Finger extension.

Innervation: Posterior interosseous nerve (C7, C8).

Blood supply: Radial recurrent artery, anterior interosseous artery, posterior interosseous artery.

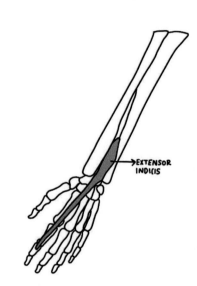

EXTENSOR POLLICIS LONGUS:

Origin: Posterior surface of middle third of ulna and interosseus membrane.

Insertion: Posterior aspect of base of distal phalanx of thumb.

Action: Wrist joints: Weak hand extension. Metacarpophalangeal and interphalangeal joint of thumb: Thumb extension.

Innervation: Posterior interosseous nerve (C7, C8).

Blood supply: Posterior interosseous artery, anterior interosseous artery.

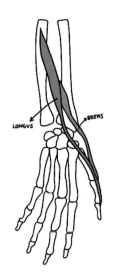

EXTENSOR POLLICIS BREVIS:

Origin: Posterior surface of distal third of radius and interosseus membrane.

Insertion: Posterior aspect of base of proximal phalanx of thumb.

Action : Carpometacarpal and metacarpophalangeal joint 1: Thumb extension.

Innervation: Posterior interosseous nerve (C7, C8).

Blood supply: Posterior interosseous artery, anterior interosseous artery.

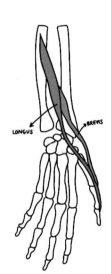

MUSCLES ABDUCTING THE WRIST:

FLEXOR CARPI RADIALIS: See page 67.

EXTENSOR CARPI RADIAIS LONGUS: See page 69.

EXTENSOR CARPI RADIALIS BREVIS: See page 69.

MUSCLES ADDUCTING THE WRIST:

FLEXOR CARPI ULNARIS: See page 67.

EXTENSOR CARPI ULNARIS: See page 69.

CHAPTER EIGHT

THE HAND

BONES OF THE HAND

On this page, we will be looking at the bones of the hand, specifically the metacarpus and the phalanges. The metacarpus is made up of five bones, the metacarpals, one corresponding to each digit and is numbered from lateral (first) to medial (fifth) sides.

THE METACARPUS:

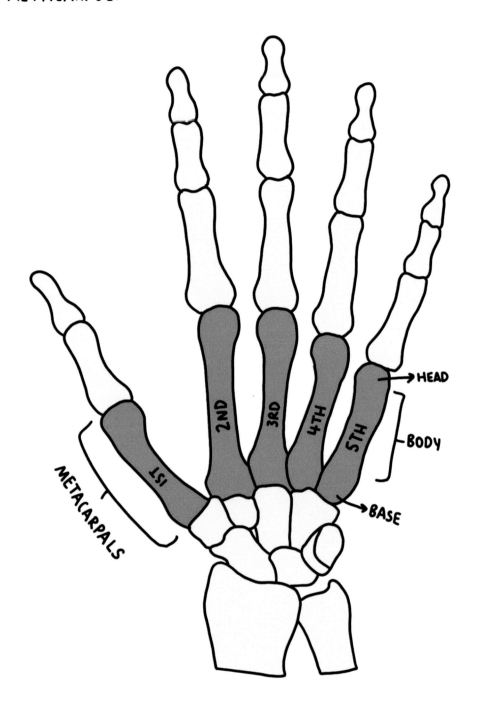

Figure 32. Illustration of the metacarpus (labelled 1-5).

QUICK FIRE QUIZ!! (Answers at the back of the book!)

What way are the metacarpals labelled 1-5?

.... to ....

BONES OF THE HAND (CONTINUED)

On this page, we will be looking at the phalanges in more detail. There are 14 phalanges in each hand, 3 for each finger, and 2 for each thumb. The phalanges of the thumb are shorter and broader than the phalanges of the fingers.

THE PHALANGES:

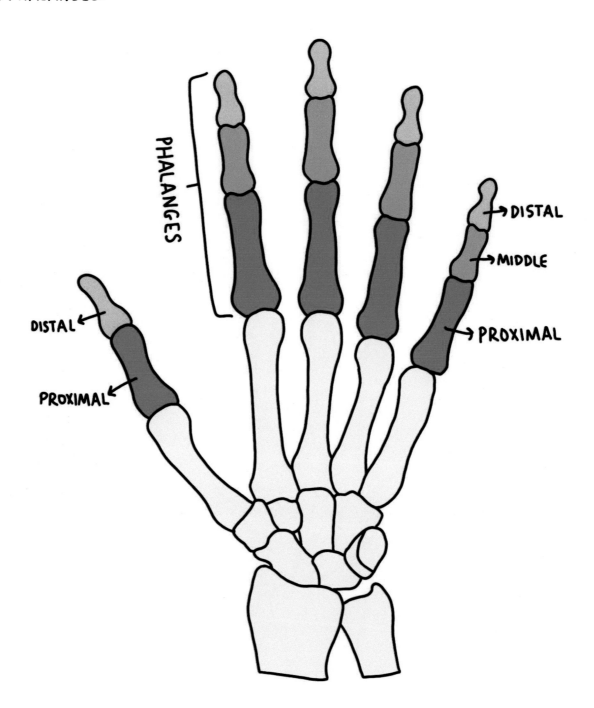

Figure 33. Illustration of the phalanges of the hand. There are 14 in each hand, 3 for each finger and 2 for the thumbs.

QUICK FIRE QUIZ!! (Answers at the back of the book!)

How many bones are there included within the phalanges on each hand?

14

JOINTS OF THE HAND

On this page, we will be discussing the different joints of the hand, including the carpometacarpal joint, the intermetacarpal joint, metacarpophalangeal joint, and the interphalangeal joint.

CARPOMETACARPAL JOINTS:

In the carpometacarpal joints, there are 5 different joints...

1. Trapeziometacarpal joint- joint between the trapezoid bone and the metacarpal bone of the thumb. (Thumb joint)
2. Carpometacarpal joint 2,3,4,5 are plane synovial joints.

TYPE	Structural classification: Synovial ellipsoid or complex saddle joints Functional classification: Synovial plane joint Degrees of freedom: CMC joints 2-3 nonaxial, CMC joints 4-5 biaxial
ARTICULAR SURFACES	CMC joint 2: Distal surfaces of trapezium, trapezoid and capitate with metacarpal 2 CMC joint 3: Distal surface of capitate with metacarpal 3 CMC joint 4: Distal surfaces of capitate and hamate with metacarpal 4 CMC joint 5: Distal surface of hamate with metacarpal 5
LIGAMENTS	Dorsal and palmar carpometacarpal ligaments, interosseous ligament
INNERVATION	Anterior and posterior interosseous nerves, deep and dorsal branches of ulnar nerve (C7-C8)
BLOOD SUPPLY	Palmar and dorsal carpal anastomoses
MOVEMENTS	CMC joints 2-3: Limited anteroposterior gliding (translation) CMC joint 4: Flexion-extension CMC joint 5: Flexion-extension, internal-external rotation

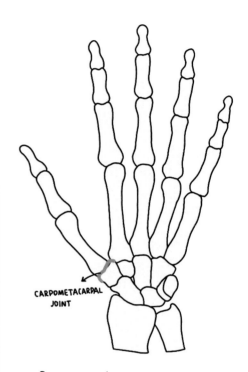

Figure 33. Illustration of the Carpometacarpal joint of the thumb.

INTERPHALANGEAL JOINTS:

- The interphalangeal joints are the joints found in between the phalanges in the fingers and thumb.

TYPE	Synovial hinge joint; uniaxial

ARTICULAR SURFACES	Head of proximal phalanx, base of middle phalanx, head of middle phalanx, and base of distal phalanx
LIGAMENTS	Medial collateral ligament, lateral collateral ligament
INNERVATION	Proper palmar digital nerves
BLOOD SUPPLY	Proper palmar digital arteries
MOVEMENTS	Flexion - extension

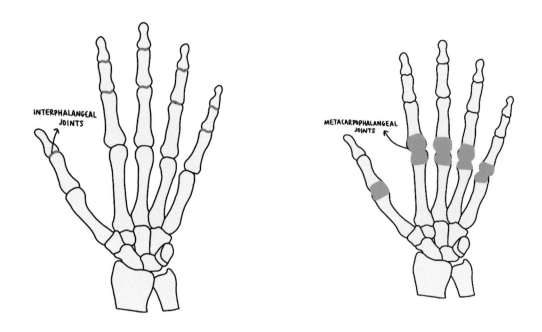

Figures 34 and 35. Illustrations of the Interphalangeal and Metacarpophalangeal joints.

METACARPOPHALANGEAL JOINT:

The metacarpophalangeal joints are condyloid joints that connect the metacarpus bones to the phalanges.

TYPE	Synovial, condyloid joint
ARTICULAR SURFACES	Heads of the distal aspect of the metacarpal bones Proximal aspects of the phalanges
LIGAMENTS	Collateral ligament, palmar ligament, deep transverse metacarpal ligaments
INNERVATION	Posterior interosseous nerve, deep terminal branch of ulnar nerve, palmar branches of median nerve
BLOOD SUPPLY	Princeps pollicis artery, radialis indicis artery, common palmar digital arteries, dorsal metacarpal arteries, palmar metacarpal arteries
MOVEMENTS	Flexion, extension, adduction, abduction, circumduction and limited rotation

QUICK FIRE QUIZ!! (Answers at the back of this book!)

What is the innervation of the interphalangeal joint?

LIGAMENTS OF THE HAND

Now we have had a look at the joints and the bones of the hand, let us take a look at the ligaments that hold all of the bones together.

DORSAL CARPOMETACARPAL LIGAMENTS: These ligaments join the carpal and metacarpal bones on their dorsal (on the back of the hand) surfaces.

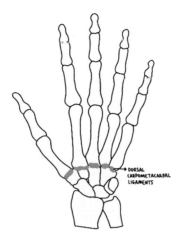

PALMAR CARPOMETACARPAL LIGAMENT: These ligaments join the carpal and metacarpal bones on their palmar (on the palm of the hand) surfaces.

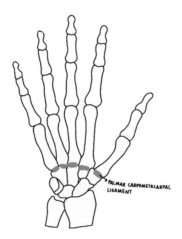

SCAPHOLUNATE INTEROSSEOUS LIGAMENT: This ligament is the link between the carpal scaphoid bone and the lunate bone.

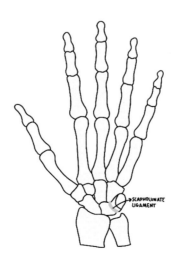

COLLATERAL LIGAMENTS: The collateral ligaments of the hand are made up of the RCL (radial collateral ligament) and the UCL (ulnar collateral ligament), these work as key stabilisers of the metacarpophalangeal joint. (See pages (enter no.) for diagrams of these ligaments.

PALMAR LIGAMENT: A ligament that is attached to the anterior margin of the base of the proximal phalanx.

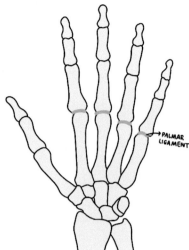

DEEP TRANSVERSE METACARPAL LIGAMENTS: This ligament connects the palmar surfaces of the heads of the 2nd, 3rd, 4th and 5th metacarpal bones.

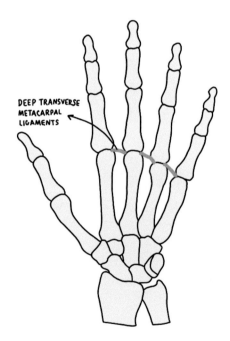

MUSCLES OF THE HAND

Now we have looked at the bones, the ligaments, and the joints of the hand, let us take a closer look at the muscles.

MUSCLES FLEXING THE FINGERS:

FLEXOR DIGITORUM SUPERFICILAIS: See page 68.

FLEXOR DIGITORUM PROFUNDUS: See page 68.

LUMBRICALS:

Origins: Tendons of flexor digitorum profundus muscle.

Insertions: Extensor expansion of hand.

Innervation: Lumbricals 1-2: Median nerve (C8-T1).
Lumbricals 3-4: Ulnar nerve (C8-T1).

Blood supply: Dorsal carpal arch (dorsal metacarpal and dorsal digital arteries), superficial palmar arch (common palmar metacarpal arteries).

Function: Metacarpophalangeal joints 2-5: Finger flexion.
Interphalangeal joints 2-5: Finger extension.

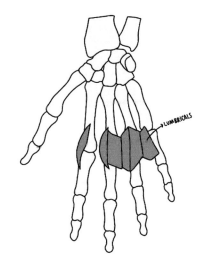

FLEXOR DIGITI MINIMI BREVIS:

Origin: Hook of hamate, flexor retinaculum.

Insertion: Base of proximal phalanx of digit 5.

Action: Metacarpophalangeal joint 5: Finger flexion (and finger lateral rotation/opposition).

Innervation: Deep branch of ulnar nerve (C8, T1).

Blood supply: Deep palmar branch of ulnar artery.

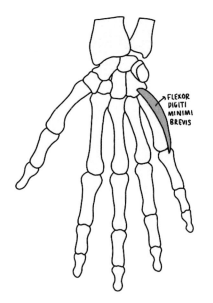

<u>MUSCLES EXTENDING THE FINGERS:</u>

EXTENSOR DIGITORUM: See page 70.

EXTENSOR DIGITI MINIMI: See page 70.

EXTENSOR INDICIS: See page 70.

DORSAL INTEROSSEI:

Origins: Adjacent sides of metacarpal bones 1-5.

Insertions: 1 and 2: Radial bases of proximal phalanges/extensor expansions of digits 2 and 3

3 and 4: Ulnar bases of proximal phalanges/extensor expansions of digits 3 and 4.

Function: Metacarpophalangeal joints 2-4: Finger abduction, finger flexion; Interphalangeal joints 2-4: Finger extension.

Innervation: Deep branch of ulnar nerve (C8-Th1).

Blood supply: 1: First dorsal metacarpal artery (radial artery) 2, 3 and 4: Second, third, and fourth dorsal metacarpal arteries (dorsal carpal anastomosis).

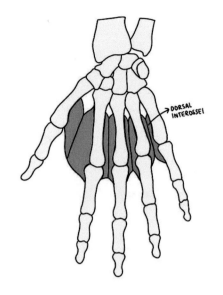

LUMBRICALS: See page 74.

MUSCLES ABDUCTING / ADDUCTING / OPPOSING THE FINGERS:

PALMAR INTEROSSEI:

Origin: Ulnar side of metacarpal bone 2, Radial side of metacarpal bones 4 and 5.

Insertion: 1: Ulnar base of proximal phalanx/extensor expansion of digit 2. 2 and 3: Radial base of proximal phalanges/extensor expansions of digits 4 and 5.

Action : Metacarpophalangeal joints 2,4 and 5: Finger adduction, Finger flexion; Interphalangeal joints 2,4 and 5: Finger extension.

Innervation: Deep branch of ulnar nerve (C8-T1).

Blood supply: Deep palmar arch, princeps pollicis artery, radialis indicis artery, palmar metacarpal arteries, proximal and distal perforating arteries, common and proper palmar arteries.

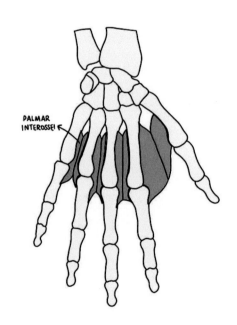

DORSAL INTEROSSEI: See top of page.

ABDUCTOR DIGITI MINIMI:

Origin: Pisiform bone (Pisohamate ligament, Tendon of flexor carpi ulnaris).

Insertion: Ulnar side of base of proximal phalanx of digit 5, Extensor expansion of digit 5.

Action: Metacarpophalangeal joint 5: Finger abduction and flexion; Interphalangeal joints: Finger extension.

Innervation: Deep branch of ulnar nerve (C8, T1).

Blood supply: Palmar branch of ulnar artery, palmar digital artery, superficial palmar arch.

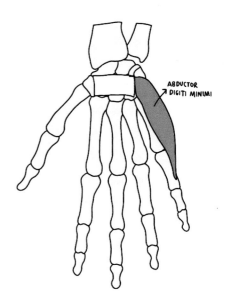

OPPONENS DIGITI MINIMI:

Origin: Hook of hamate bone, flexor retinaculum.

Insertion: Ulnar aspect of metacarpal bone 5.

Action: Carpometacarpal joint 5: Finger flexion, finger lateral rotation/opposition.

Innervation: Deep branch of ulnar nerve (C8, T1).

Blood supply: Deep palmar branch of ulnar artery, deep palmar arch.

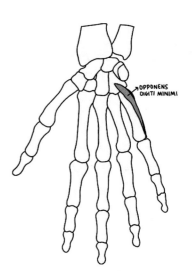

MUSCLES FLEXING THE THUMB:

FLEXOR POLLICIS LONGUS: (See page (enter no.))

FLEXOR POLLICIS BREVIS:

Origin: Superficial head: Flexor retinaculum, tubercle of trapezium bone. Deep head: Trapezoid and capitate bones.

Insertion: Lateral aspect of base of proximal phalanx 1 (via radial sesamoid bone).

Action: Carpometacarpal and metacarpophalangeal joint 1: Thumb flexion.

Innervation: Superficial head: Recurrent branch of median nerve. Deep head: Deep branch of ulnar nerve (C8, T1).

Blood supply: Superficial palmar artery, princeps pollicis artery and radialis indicis artery.

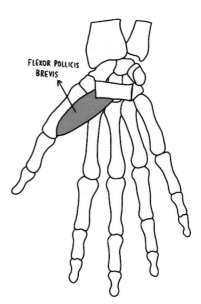

MUSCLES EXTENDING THE THUMB:

EXTENSOR POLLICIS LONGUS: See page 68.

EXTENSOR POLLICIS BREVIS: See page 71.

MUSCLES ABDUCTING / ADDUCTING / OPPOSING THE THUMB:

ABDUCTOR POLLICIS LONGUS:

Origin: Posterior surface of proximal half of radius, ulna and interosseus membrane.

Insertion: Base of metacarpal bone 1, (trapezium bone).

Action: Radiocarpal joint: Hand extension; Carpometacarpal joint of thumb: Thumb abduction and extension.

Innervation: Posterior interosseous nerve (C7, C8).

Blood supply: Anterior interosseous artery, posterior interosseous artery.

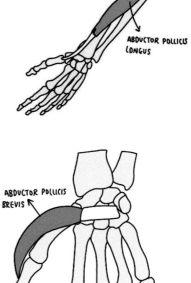

ABDUCTOR POLLICIS LONGUS

ABDUCTOR POLLICIS BREVIS:

Origin: Tubercles of scaphoid and trapezium bones, Flexor retinaculum.

Insertion: Lateral aspect of base of proximal phalanx 1 (via radial sesamoid bone).

Action : Carpometacarpal joint 1: Thumb abduction.

Innervation: Recurrent branch of median nerve (C8, T1).

Blood supply: Superficial palmar branch of radial artery.

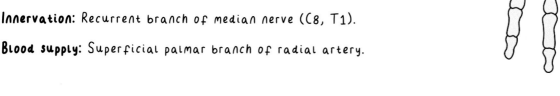

ABDUCTOR POLLICIS BREVIS

OPPONENS POLLICIS:

Origin: Tubercle of trapezium bone, flexor retinaculum.

Insertion: Radial border of metacarpal bone 1.

Action : Carpometacarpal joint 1: Thumb opposition.

Innervation: Recurrent branch of median nerve (C8, T1).

Blood supply: Superficial palmar branch of radial artery.

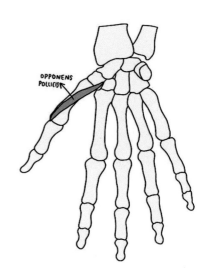

OPPONENS POLLICIS

PALMARIS BREVIS:

Origin: Palmar aponeurosis, flexor retinaculum.

Insertion: Dermis of skin of hypothenar region.

Action : Tightens palmar aponeurosis, tightens grip.

Innervation: Superficial branch of ulnar nerve (C8, T1).

Blood supply: Superficial palmar arch.

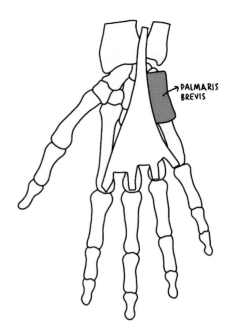

PALMARIS BREVIS

QUICK FIRE QUIZ!! (Answers at the back of book!)

What is the insertion for the Abductor Pollicis Longus muscle?

....

CHAPTER NINE

THE BRACHIAL PLEXUS AND NERVES OF THE UPPER LIMB

BRACHIAL PLEXUS AND NERVES OF THE UPPER LIMB

BRACHIAL PLEXUS:

Roots: C5, C6, C7, C8, T1.

Trunks: Superior trunk, Middle trunk, Inferior trunk.

Divisions: Three anterior divisions: Anterior division of superior trunk, Anterior division of middle trunk, Anterior division of inferior trunk. Three posterior divisions: Posterior division of superior trunk, Posterior division of middle trunk, Posterior division of inferior trunk.

Cords: Lateral, Medial, Posterior.

Terminal branches: Musculocutaneous nerve, Axillary nerve, Radial nerve, Median nerve, Ulnar nerve.

Innervation: Complete sensory and motor innervation of the arm.

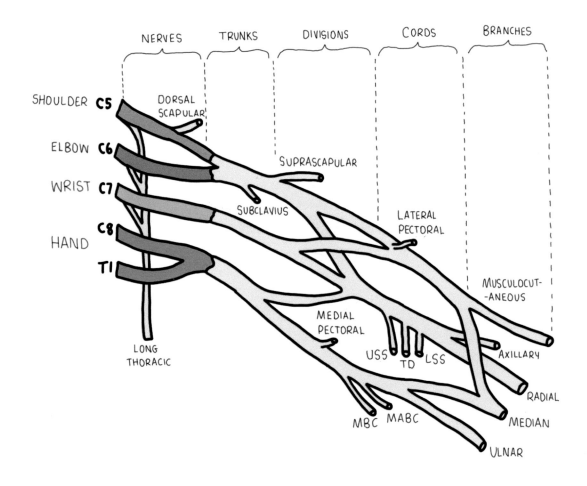

Figure 36. Illustration of the Brachial Plexus.

AXILLARY NERVE:

Origin: Posterior cord of brachial plexus (C5-C6).

Branches: Anterior, posterior, articular branches.

Innervation: Motor - deltoid muscle, teres minor muscle, lateral head of the triceps brachii muscle. Sensory - glenohumeral joint, skin of the deltoid region/upper arm.

Clinical relations: Neuropathy, quadrangular space syndrome.

MUSCULOCUTANEOUS NERVE:

Origin: Brachial plexus (C5-C7).

Supply area: Coracobrachialis, biceps brachii and brachialis muscles.

Clinical relations: Brachial plexus injury.

ULNAR NERVE:

Origin: Brachial plexus (C8-T1).

Branches: Muscular branches, articular branches, palmer cutaneous branch, dorsal cutaneous branch, superficial branch, deep branch.

Supply: Motor: Flexor carpi ulnaris and medial half of flexor digitorum profundus. Most of the intrinsic hand muscles. Sensory: Anterior aspect of the ulnar 1 and a half fingers (little finger and half of the ring finger) and medial palmar skin. Dorsal aspect of the ulnar 1 and a half fingers and medial aspect of dorsum of hand.

RADIAL NERVE:

Origin: Posterior cord of brachial plexus (C5-T1).

Branches: Posterior brachial cutaneous nerve, inferior lateral brachial cutaneous nerve, posterior antebrachial cutaneous nerve, muscular branches, deep branch of radial nerve, superficial branch of radial nerve.

Supply : Motor: triceps brachii, anconeus, brachioradialis, extensor carpi radialis longus, extensor carpi radialis brevis, supinator, extensor digitorum, extensor digiti minimi, extensor carpi ulnaris, abductor pollicis longus, extensor pollicis brevis, extensor pollicis longus, extensor indicis. Sensory: lower outer aspect and posterior surface of the arm, central and posterior aspect of the forearm, thenar eminence and dorsal aspect of the radial three and half digits of the hand.

MEDIAN NERVE:

Origin: Medial and lateral cords of brachial plexus (C5-T1).

Supply: Pronator teres, flexor carpi radialis, palmaris longus, flexor digitorum superficialis, abductor pollicis brevis, flexor pollicis brevis, opponens pollicis, lateral two lumbricals. From anterior interosseous nerve: Flexor pollicis longus, lateral half flexor digitorum profundus.

THE DERMATOMES OF THE UPPER LIMB:

Dermatomes of the upper limbs are innervated by spinal nerves C5-T2. Here, the organisation of dermatomes is complex because of how the upper limbs bud in embryonic development.

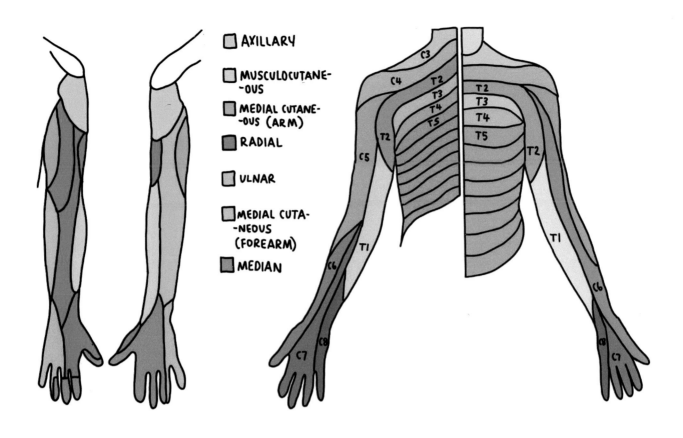

Figure 37. Illustration of the Dermatomes of the Upper Limb and the Cutaneous nerve supply.

C5 - anterior skin below the clavicles spreading over the lateral aspect of the upper limb, posterior skin around the base of the neck.

C6 - shoulders and longitudinally down the middle posterior aspect of the upper limb, radial side of the hand, thumb.

C7 - hand, middle finger.

C8 - ulnar side of the hand, ring finger, and little finger.

T1 - level of the infraclavicular fossa, extending to the medial aspect of the forearm.

T2 - anterior and posteriorly extends at the level of the upper axilla and medial and upper aspect of the arm.

QUICK FIRE QUIZ!! (Answers at the back of book!)

What is the origin of the Axillary Nerve?

....

What is the area that C7 covers in Dermatomes?

....

CHAPTER TEN

BLOOD SUPPLY OF THE UPPER LIMB

BLOOD SUPPLY OF THE UPPER LIMB

On this page we will be discussing the blood supply of the upper limb, from the veins and the arteries! Let us start by taking a look at the arteries...

ARTERIES OF UPPER LIMB:

SUBCLAVIAN ARTERY:

Origin: Aortic arch (left side of the body), brachiocephalic trunk (right side of the body).

Continuation: Axillary artery.

Thoracic region branches: Vertebral artery- Internal thoracic artery: superior epigastric, pericardiophrenic, musculophrenic arteries. Thyrocervical trunk: inferior thyroid artery, ascending cervical, transverse cervical, suprascapular arteries.

Muscular region branches: Costocervical trunk: supreme intercostal, deep cervical arteries.

Cervical region branches: Deep branch of the transverse cervical artery.

AXILLARY ARTERY:

Source: Subclavian artery.

Branches: Superior thoracic, Thoracoacromial, Lateral thoracic, Anterior circumflex humeral, Posterior circumflex humeral, Subscapular.

Vein: The axillary vein.

Supplies: The axilla, upper limb, lateral thoracic region.

BRACHIAL ARTERY:

Source: Axillary artery.

Branches: Profunda brachii, Nutrient artery of the humerus, Superior ulnar collateral artery, Middle ulnar collateral artery, Inferior ulnar collateral artery, Deltoid artery, Radial artery, Ulnar artery.

Vein: Brachial vein.

Supplies: Biceps brachii, triceps brachii, coracobrachialis muscles.

Clinical relations: Brachial pulse, blood pressure, injury by supracondylar fracture, compression, ischaemic compartment syndrome.

RADIAL ARTERY:

Source: Brachial artery.

Branches: Muscular branches, radial recurrent artery, palmar carpal branch, dorsal carpal branch, superficial palmar branch, deep palmar branch, first dorsal metacarpal artery, princeps pollicis artery, radialis indicis artery.

Clinical relations: Radial arterial pulse, Allens test.

ULNAR ARTERY:

Source: Brachial artery.

Branches: Anterior ulnar recurrent, Posterior ulnar recurrent, Common interosseous, Dorsal carpal branch, Deep palmar branch, Palmar carpal branch.

Supply area: Medial aspect of the forearm, medial aspect of the hand.

SUPERFICIAL PALMAR ARCH:

Origin: Ulnar artery, superficial palmar branch of radial artery.

Branches: Common palmar digital arteries.

Supply : Proximal, middle and distal phalanges of digits 2-4, metacarpophalangeal and interphalangeal joints of digits 2-4, soft tissue of digits 2-4.

DEEP PALMAR ARCH:

Origin: Direct continuation of radial artery with a medial contribution from ulnar artery.

Branches: Palmar metacarpal arteries, perforating branches, recurrent branches.

Supply: Carpal bones, metacarpal bones, adjacent muscles of the hand, metacarpophalangeal and proximal interphalangeal joints, radioulnar joint.

Figures 38 and 39. Illustrations of the arteries and veins of the upper limb.

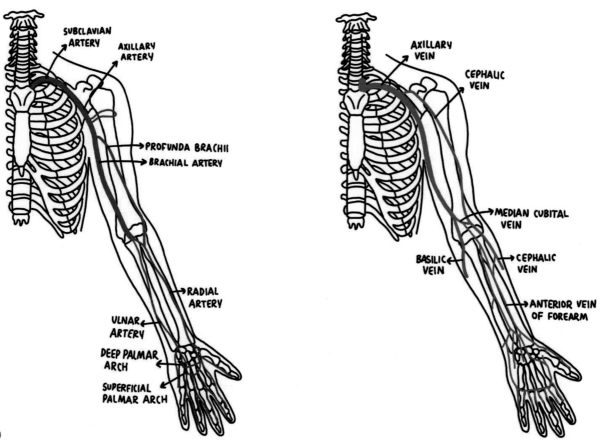

AXILLARY VEIN:

Drains from: Confluence of brachial and basilic vein.

Branches: Subscapular, circumflex humeral, lateral thoracic, thoracoacromial, cephalic vein.

Drains to: Subclavian vein.

Drainage area: Thorax, axilla, upper limb.

DORSAL VENOUS ARCH:

Predominant drainage route of the hand (also receiving palmar venous return via perforating veins). Gives rise to cephalic and basilic veins.

BASILIC VEIN:

Source: Dorsal venous network of the hand.

Empties into: Brachial vein.

Draining area: Parts of the hand and forearm.

CEPHALIC VEIN:

Source: Dorsal venous network of the hand.

Empties into: Axillary vein.

Drainage area: Radial parts of the hand, forearm and arm.

Clinical relations: Cephalic vein cutdown, Housemans friend, varicose veins.

MEDIAN CUBITAL VEIN:

Drains from: Cephalic vein.

Branches: Median antebrachial vein.

Drains to: Basilic vein, brachial veins.

Drainage area: Hand, wrist, forearm.

ANTERIOR MEDIAN VEIN OF THE FOREARM:

Drains from: Venous plexus on palmar surface of hand.

Branches: Small superficial veins of the forearm.

Drains to: Basilic and median cubital veins.

Drainage area: Palmar (volar) surface of the forearm and hand.

CHAPTER
ELEVEN

THE PECTORAL GIRDLE
pewic

INTRODUCTION TO THE LOWER LIMB AND PELVIC GIRDLE

The pelvic girdle is made up of several different bones. It is composed of the innominates and the sacrum. The innominate is made up of 3 bones: the ilium, the ischium and pubis. It also contains the coccyx bone. Let us start by taking a closer look at the overall structure of the lower limb.

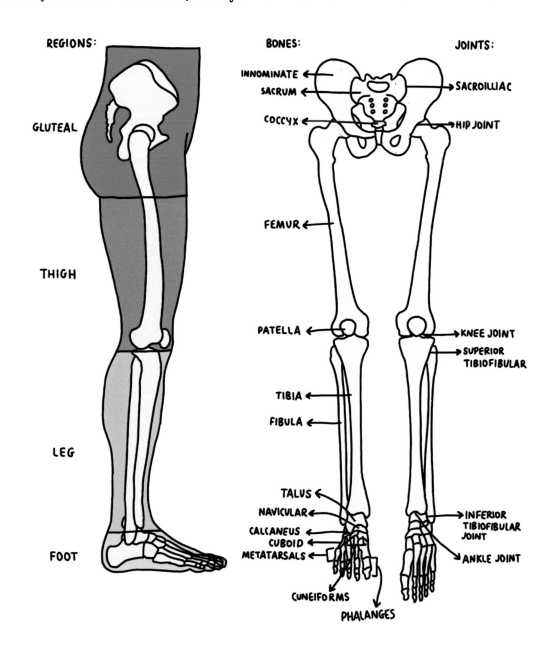

Figure 40. Illustration of the bones, regions and joints of the lower limb.

Make sure to take a good look at this diagram and understand where the different areas of the lower limb are. In this chapter we will be focussing on the pelvic girdle, so make sure you are aware where these bones lie, and what structures surround them etc.

QUICK FIRE QUIZ!! (Answers at the back of this book!)

Which bones are included within the pelvic girdle?

A. The innominate and sacrum
B. The ilium and sacrum
C. The innominate
D. The femur

BONES OF THE PELVIC GIRDLE (CONTINUED)

Now we have looked at the more generic view of the lower limb, let us take a closer look at the area of the pelvic girdle in more detail.

THE INNOMINATE:

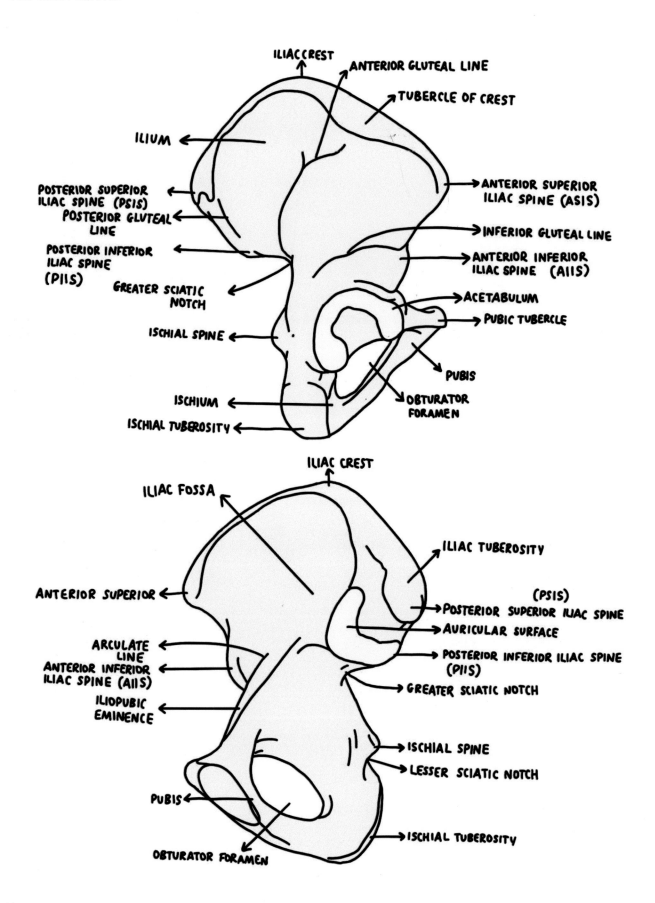

ILIAC CREST

ANTERIOR GLUTEAL LINE

TUBERCLE OF CREST

ILIUM

POSTERIOR SUPERIOR ILIAC SPINE (PSIS)

POSTERIOR GLUTEAL LINE

POSTERIOR INFERIOR ILIAC SPINE (PIIS)

GREATER SCIATIC NOTCH

ISCHIAL SPINE

ISCHIUM

ISCHIAL TUBEROSITY

ANTERIOR SUPERIOR ILIAC SPINE (ASIS)

INFERIOR GLUTEAL LINE

ANTERIOR INFERIOR ILIAC SPINE (AIIS)

ACETABULUM

PUBIC TUBERCLE

PUBIS

OBTURATOR FORAMEN

ILIAC CREST

ILIAC FOSSA

ILIAC TUBEROSITY

ANTERIOR SUPERIOR

(PSIS)

POSTERIOR SUPERIOR ILIAC SPINE

AURICULAR SURFACE

ARCULATE LINE

ANTERIOR INFERIOR ILIAC SPINE (AIIS)

ILIOPUBIC EMINENCE

POSTERIOR INFERIOR ILIAC SPINE (PIIS)

GREATER SCIATIC NOTCH

ISCHIAL SPINE

LESSER SCIATIC NOTCH

PUBIS

ISCHIAL TUBEROSITY

OBTURATOR FORAMEN

THE SACRUM AND THE COCCYX:

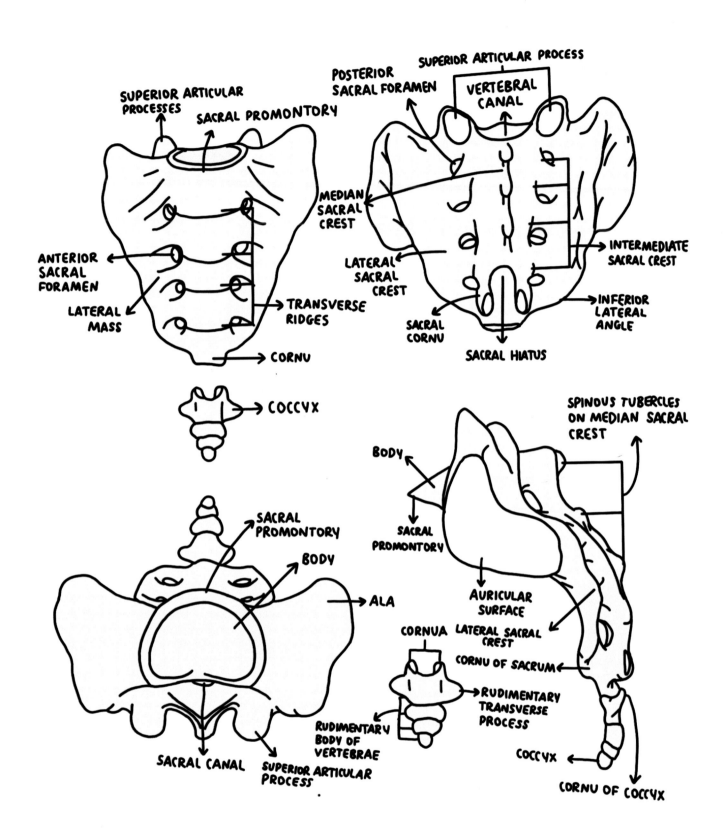

SUPERIOR ARTICULAR PROCESSES

SACRAL PROMONTORY

POSTERIOR SACRAL FORAMEN

SUPERIOR ARTICULAR PROCESS

VERTEBRAL CANAL

MEDIAN SACRAL CREST

ANTERIOR SACRAL FORAMEN

LATERAL MASS

TRANSVERSE RIDGES

CORNU

LATERAL SACRAL CREST

INTERMEDIATE SACRAL CREST

INFERIOR LATERAL ANGLE

SACRAL CORNU

SACRAL HIATUS

COCCYX

SPINOUS TUBERCLES ON MEDIAN SACRAL CREST

BODY

SACRAL PROMONTORY

BODY

ALA

SACRAL PROMONTORY

AURICULAR SURFACE

CORNUA

LATERAL SACRAL CREST

CORNU OF SACRUM

RUDIMENTARY TRANSVERSE PROCESS

RUDIMENTARY BODY OF VERTEBRAE

COCCYX

CORNU OF COCCYX

SACRAL CANAL

SUPERIOR ARTICULAR PROCESS

QUICK FIRE QUIZ!! (Answers at the back of this book!)

Can you name a structure found within the innominate?

....

95

JOINTS OF THE PELVIC GIRDLE:

On this page we will be taking a look at the joints of the pelvic girdle, including some cartilaginous joints (such as the pubic symphysis).

THE SACROILIAC JOINT:

TYPE	Synovial plane joint; nonaxial
ARTICULAR SURFACES	Auricular surface of ilium, auricular surface of sacrum
LIGAMENTS	Anterior sacroiliac ligament, posterior sacroiliac ligament (short, long and interosseous sacroiliac ligament); sacrotuberous ligament, sacrospinous ligament
INNERVATION	S1–S2 spinal nerves, superior gluteal nerve, obturator nerve, lumbosacral trunk
BLOOD SUPPLY	Iliolumbar, superior gluteal, lateral sacral arteries
MOVEMENTS	Slight gliding and rotatory movements

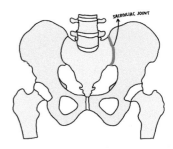

Figure 41. Illustration of the sacroiliac joint.

THE PUBIC SYMPHYSIS JOINT:

The pubic symphysis is a secondary cartilaginous joint between the medial surfaces of the pubic bones. The surfaces are lined with a layer of hyaline cartilage and connected by the fibrous symphyseal cartilage interposed between them. Usually, there are no movements on this joint, except in pregnancy when the ligaments and cartilage soften, allowing the increase of pelvic diameters during labor.

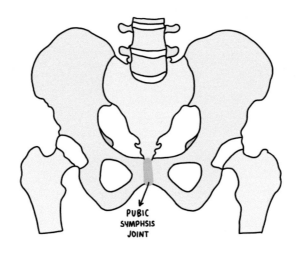

Figure 42. Illustration of the pubic symphysis joint.

THE LUMBOSACRAL JOINT:

TYPE	Anterior intervertebral joint: symphysis Facet joints: synovial plane joints
ARTICULAR SURFACES	Anterior intervertebral joint: Inferior surface of L5 vertebral body, superior surface of S1 vertebral body Facet joints: superior articular processes of the S1, inferior articular processes of L5
LIGAMENTS	Iliolumbar ligament, lateral lumbosacral ligament
INNERVATION	L5 and S1 spinal nerves
BLOOD SUPPLY	Iliolumbar, superior lateral and median sacral arteries
MOVEMENTS	Flexion, extension, lateral flexion

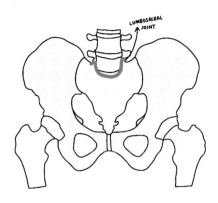

Figure 43. Illustration of the lumbosacral joint.

THE SACROCOCCYGEAL JOINT:

TYPE	Secondary cartilaginous joint (symphysis)
ARTICULAR SURFACES	Apex of sacrum, the base of coccyx
LIGAMENTS	Anterior sacrococcygeal, superior posterior sacrococcygeal, deep posterior sacrococcygeal, lateral sacrococcygeal, intercornual ligaments
INNERVATION	Spinal nerves S4-Co
BLOOD SUPPLY	Inferior lateral sacral, median sacral arteries
MOVEMENTS	Passive flexion and extension

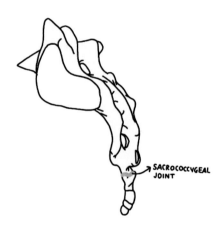

Figure 44. Illustration of the sacrococcygeal joint.

QUICK FIRE QUIZ!! (Answers at the back of this book!)

What is the innervation of the sacroiliac joint?

....

Can you name 1 or 2 ligaments that are involved in the lumbosacral joint?

1.   2.

LIGAMENTS OF THE PELVIC GIRDLE:

ANTERIOR SACROILIAC LIGAMENT: The anterior sacroiliac ligament connects the front of the ilium to the front of the sacrum and the preauricular sulcus.

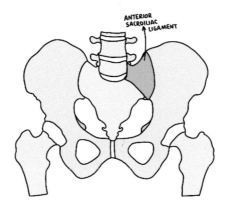

POSTERIOR SACROILIAC LIGAMENT (SHORT, LONG AND INTEROSSEOUS SACROILIAC LIGAMENT): The posterior sacroiliac ligament is located behind the pelvis and connects the sacrum with the ilium. (See image below for location of these ligaments)

SACROTUBEROUS LIGAMENT: This ligament is located posterior inferiorly in the pelvis between the sacrum and ischial tuberosity, where most of its band inserts into ischial tuberosity forming with sacrospinous ligament the boundary to the greater and lesser sciatic notch.

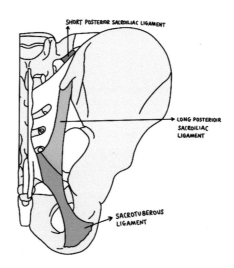

Figure 44. Illustration of the posterior sacroiliac ligaments and the Sacrotuberous ligaments.

SACROSPINOUS LIGAMENT: The sacrospinous ligament is a thin ligament attached to the ischial spine (a bone prominence in the lower pelvis) and the lateral (side) regions of the sacrum (at the bottom of the spine) and coccyx, or tailbone.

See image to the right for diagram of this ligament.

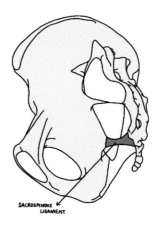

ILIOLUMBAR LIGAMENT: The iliolumbar ligament is a strong ligament passing from the tip of the transverse process of the fifth lumbar vertebra to the posterior part of the inner lip of the iliac crest (upper margin of ilium).

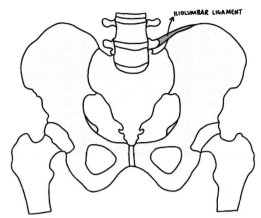

LATERAL LUMBOSACRAL LIGAMENT: This ligament arises from the lower margin of the transverse process of L5 vertebra and passes obliquely inferiorly to attach on the ala of the sacrum.

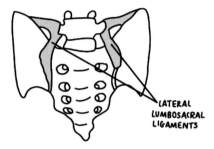

ANTERIOR SACROCOCCYGEAL LIGAMENT: This ligament consists of a few irregular fibres, which descend from the anterior surface of the sacrum to the front of the coccyx, blending with the periosteum. (Internal so hard to see on a diagram!)

SUPERIOR POSTERIOR SACROCOCCYGEAL LIGAMENT: This ligament arises from the margin of the sacral hiatus and attaches to the dorsal surface of the coccyx.

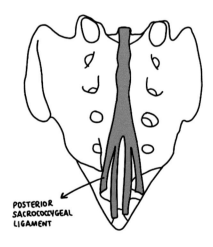

DEEP POSTERIOR SACROCOCCYGEAL LIGAMENT: This ligament spans from the dorsal surface of the fifth sacral segment to the dorsal surface of coccyx. (This is also too deep to be seen on a diagram!)

LATERAL SACROCOCCYGEAL LIGAMENTS: A pair of ligaments stretching from the lower lateral angles of the sacrum to the transverse processes of the first coccygeal vertebra.

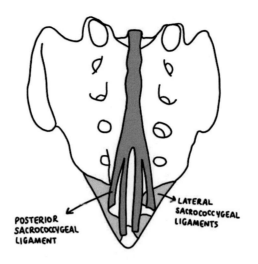

INTERCORNUAL LIGAMENTS: This ligament stretches from the cornu of the sacrum (The two small processes projecting inferiorly) to the cornu of the coccyx. (Too deep to be viewed on a diagram)

SUPERIOR PUBIC LIGAMENT: This ligament connects the 2 pubic bones superiorly.

ARCUATE PUBIC LIGAMENT: This ligament connects the 2 pubic bones inferiorly.

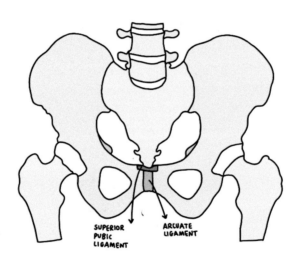

QUICK FIRE QUIZ!! (Answers at the end of this book!)

Describe the position of the superior posterior sacrococcygeal ligament.

....

....

CHAPTER TWELVE

THE HIP

BONES OF THE HIP

On this page we will be looking at the bones that make up the hip joint. The femur is the strongest and largest bone found within the human body! The femur is the main bone that makes up the hip joint, it articulates with the acetabulum of the innominate.

THE FEMUR:

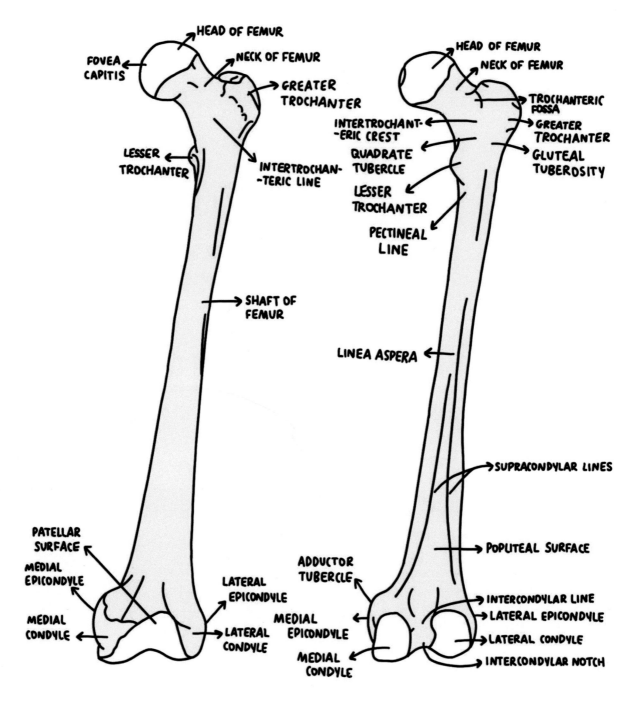

Figure 45. Illustration of the left femur bone (anteriorly and posteriorly).

QUICK FIRE QUIZ!! (Answers at the back of this book!)

Fill in the blanks:

The femur is the .... and .... bone in the human body.

THE HIP JOINT

Now we have looked at the main bone which makes up the hip joint, we will take a closer look at the hip joint itself!

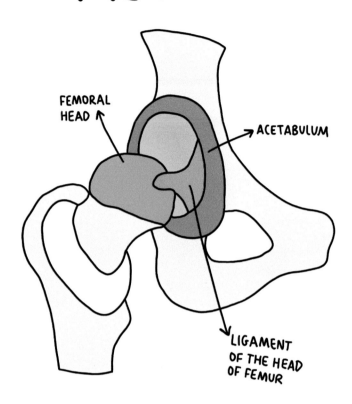

THE HIP JOINT:

Figure 46. Illustration of the hip joint.

TYPE	Synovial ball and socket; multiaxial
ARTICULAR SURFACES	Head of femur, lunate surface of acetabulum
LIGAMENTS	Capsular: iliofemoral, pubofemoral, ischiofemoral Intracapsular: transverse ligament of the acetabulum, ligament of the head of the femur
INNERVATION	Femoral nerve, obturator nerve, superior gluteal nerve, nerve to quadratus femoris
BLOOD SUPPLY	Medial and lateral circumflex femoral arteries, obturator artery, superior and inferior gluteal arteries
MOVEMENTS	Flexion, extension, abduction, adduction, external rotation, internal rotation and circumduction

QUICK FIRE QUIZ!! (Answers at the back of book!)

What is the blood supply of the hip joint? Can you name at least one main artery?

THE LIGAMENTS OF THE HIP JOINT

ILIOFEMORAL LIGAMENT: A ligament of the hip joint which extends from the ilium to the femur in front of the joint. (It is also sometimes referred to as the Y ligament due to the shape it takes.)

PUBOFEMORAL LIGAMENT: A ligament that extends from the pubic portion of the acetabular rim and passes below the neck of the femur.

ISCHIOFEMORAL LIGAMENT: A ligament that fibres span from the ischium at a point below and behind the acetabulum to blend with the circular fibres at the posterior end of the joint capsule and attach at the intertrochanteric line of the femur.

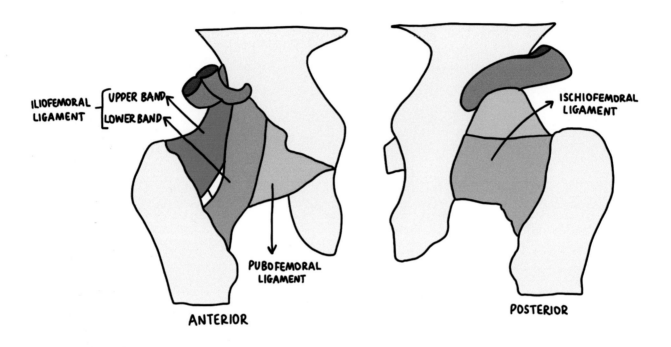

Figure 47. Illustration of the iliofemoral, the Ischiofemoral, and the pubofemoral ligaments of the hip.

TRANSVERSE LIGAMENT OF THE ACETABULUM: The transverse ligament of the hip bridges the acetabular notch (located anteroinferiorly along the margin of the acetabulum) and joins the two ends of the acetabular labrum, thus forming a complete ring. Beneath it (through the acetabular foramen) pass nutrient vessels which enter the ligamentum teres which arises from the transverse ligament.

LIGAMENTUM TERES: A ligament that connects the femoral head to the acetabulum. It is an important in providing hip stability and supplies blood to the femoral head.

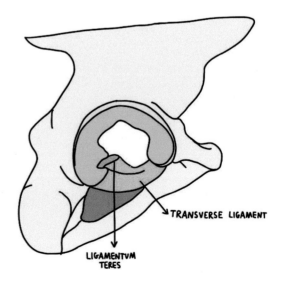

Figure 48. Illustration of the transverse ligament and the ligamentum teres.

QUICK FIRE QUIZ!! (Answers at the back of this book!)

Describe the pathway of the transverse ligament of the acetabulum.

....

....

....

....

MUSCLES OF THE HIP JOINT

Now we have looked at the bones, the joint itself and the ligaments of the hip, we will finally take a look at the muscles involved in the movements of the hip joint.

MUSCLES FLEXING THE HIP JOINT:

PSOAS MAJOR:

Origin: Vertebral bodies of T12-L4, intervertebral discs between T12-L4, transverse processes of L1-L5 vertebrae.

Insertion: Lesser trochanter of femur as iliopsoas tendon.

Action: Hip joint: Flexion of the thigh/trunk, lateral rotation of the thigh. Lateral flexion of the trunk.

Innervation: Anterior rami of spinal nerves L1-L3.

Blood supply: Lumbar branch of iliolumbar artery.

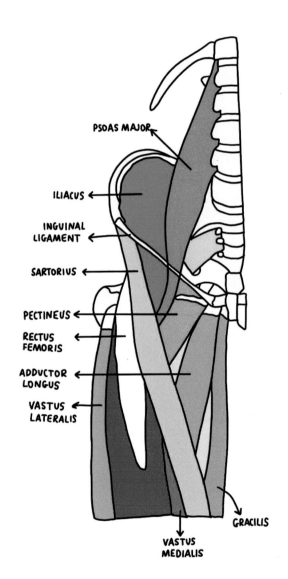

ILIACUS:

Origin: Iliac fossa.

Insertion: Lesser trochanter of femur.

Action: Hip joint: Thigh/trunk flexion.

Innervation: Femoral nerve (L1-L3).

Blood supply: Iliolumbar, deep circumflex iliac, obturator, and femoral arteries.

PECTINEUS:

Origin: Superior pubic ramus (pectineal line of pubis).

Insertion: Pectineal line of femur, linea aspera of femur.

Figure 49. Illustration of the Anterior portion of the thigh- including all of the muscles that flex the hip joint.

Action: Hip joint: Thigh flexion, thigh adduction, thigh external rotation, thigh internal rotation; pelvis stabilization.

Innervation: Femoral nerve (L2, L3) (Obturator nerve (L2, L3)).

Blood supply: Medial femoral circumflex artery, obturator artery.

RECTUS FEMORIS:

Origin: Anterior inferior iliac spine, supraacetabular groove.

Insertion: Tibial tuberosity (via patellar ligament), patella.

Action: Hip joint: Thigh flexion; Knee joint: Leg extension.

Innervation: Femoral nerve (L2-L4).

Blood supply: Femoral, lateral femoral circumflex, superficial circumflex iliac arteries.

SARTORIUS:

Origin: Anterior superior iliac spine (ASIS).

Insertion: Proximal end of tibia below medial condyle (via pes anserinus).

Innervation: Femoral nerve (L2-L3).

Blood supply: Proximal third: branches of femoral artery, deep femoral artery, artery of quadriceps, lateral circumflex femoral artery. Middle third: branches of femoral artery. Distal third: branches of femoral and descending genicular arteries**Function:** Hip joint: thigh flexion, thigh abduction, thigh external rotation. Knee joint: leg flexion, leg internal rotation.

MUSCLES EXTENDING THE HIP JOINT:
GLUTEUS MAXIMUS:

Origin: Lateroposterior surface of sacrum and coccyx, gluteal surface of ilium (behind posterior gluteal line), thoracolumbar fascia, Sacrotuberous ligament.

Insertion: Iliotibial tract, gluteal tuberosity of femur.

Action: Hip joint: Thigh extension, thigh external rotation, thigh abduction (superior part), thigh adduction (inferior part).

Innervation: Inferior gluteal nerve (L5, S1, S2).

Blood supply: Inferior gluteal and superior gluteal arteries.

THE HAMSTRINGS:
SEMITENDINOSUS:

Origin: (Posteromedial impression of) Ischial tuberosity.

Insertion: Proximal end of tibia below medial condyle (via pes anserinus).

Action: Hip joint: Thigh extension, thigh internal rotation, stabilizes pelvis. Knee joint: Leg flexion, leg internal rotation.

Innervation: Tibial division of sciatic nerve (L5-S2).

Blood supply: First perforating branch of deep femoral artery, medial femoral circumflex artery, inferior gluteal artery and inferior medial geniculate artery.

SEMIMEMBRANOSUS:

Origin: Superolateral impression of ischial tuberosity.

Insertion: Medial condyle of tibia.

Action: Hip joint: thigh extension and internal rotation. Knee joint: flexion and internal rotation of the leg. Stabilizes pelvis.

Innervation: Tibial division of sciatic nerve (L5 — S2).

Blood supply: Perforating branches of femoral and popliteal arteries.

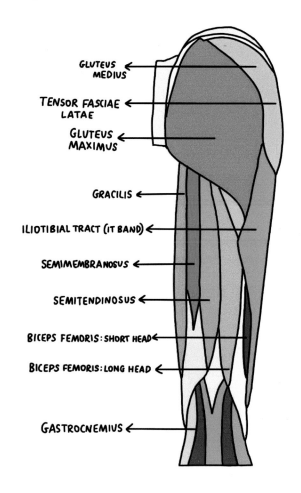

Figure 50. Illustration of the posterior portion of the thigh muscles.

BICEPS FEMORIS:

Origin: Long head: (inferomedial impression of) ischial tuberosity, sacrotuberous ligament. Short head: linea aspera of femur (lateral lip), lateral supracondylar line of femur.

Insertion: (Lateral aspect of) head of fibula.

Action: Hip joint: thigh extension, thigh external rotation; Knee joint: leg flexion, leg external rotation; stabilizes pelvis.

Innervation: Long head: tibial division of sciatic nerve (L5-S2). Short head: common fibular division of sciatic nerve (L5-S2).

Blood supply: Inferior gluteal artery, perforating arteries, popliteal artery.

<u>MUSCLES ABDUCTING THE HIP JOINT:</u>

GLUTEUS MAXIMUS: See page 106.

GLUTEUS MEDIUS:

Origin: Gluteal surface of ilium (between anterior and posterior gluteal lines).

Insertion: Lateral aspect of greater trochanter of femur.

Action: Hip joint: Thigh abduction, thigh internal rotation (anterior part); Pelvis stabilization.

Innervation: Superior gluteal nerve (L4-S1).

Blood supply: Deep branch of superior gluteal artery, trochanteric anastomosis.

GLUTEUS MINIMUS:

Origin: Gluteal surface of ilium (between anterior and inferior gluteal lines).

Insertion: Anterior aspect of greater trochanter of femur.

Action: Hip joint: Thigh abduction, thigh internal rotation (anterior part); Pelvis stabilization.

Innervation: Superior gluteal nerve (L4-S1).

Blood supply: Superior gluteal artery, trochanteric anastomosis.

TENSOR FASCIA LATAE: (See figure 50)

Origin: Outer lip of anterior iliac crest, Anterior superior iliac spine (ASIS).

Insertion: Iliotibial tract.

Action: Hip joint: Thigh internal rotation, (Weak abduction); Knee joint: Leg external rotation, (Weak leg flexion/ extension); Stabilizes hip and knee joints.

Innervation: Superior gluteal nerve (L4-S1).

Blood supply: Ascending branch of lateral circumflex femoral artery.

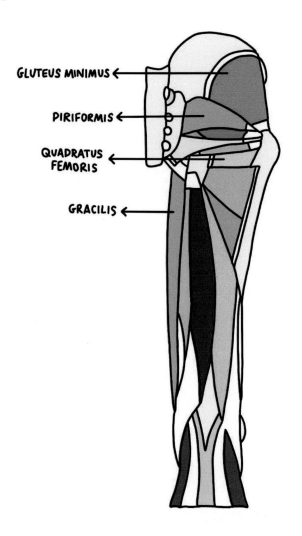

Figure 51. Illustration of the posterior portion of the thigh muscles.

MUSCLES ADDUCTING THE HIP JOINT:

ADDUCTOR MAGNUS:

Origin: Adductor part: Inferior pubic ramus, ischial ramus. Ischiocondylar part: Ischial tuberosity.

Insertion: Adductor part: Gluteal tuberosity, linea aspera (medial lip), medial supracondylar line. Ischiocondylar part: Adductor tubercle of femur.

Action: Adductor part: Hip joint - Thigh flexion, thigh adduction, thigh external rotation. Hamstring part: Hip joint - Thigh extension, thigh internal rotation. Entire muscle: Pelvis stabilization.

Innervation: Adductor part: Obturator nerve (L2-L4). Ischiocondylar part: Tibial division of sciatic nerve (L4).

108

Blood supply: Deep femoral artery; Femoral, popliteal and genicular arteries.

ADDUCTOR LONGUS:

Origin: Body of pubis, inferior to pubic crest and lateral to the pubic symphysis.

Insertion: Middle third of linea aspera of femur (medial lip).

Action: Hip joint: Thigh flexion, Thigh adduction, Thigh external rotation; Pelvis stabilization.

Innervation: Obturator nerve (L2-L4).

Blood supply: Profunda femoris artery, obturator artery.

ADDUCTOR BREVIS:

Origin: Anterior body of pubis, inferior pubic ramus.

Insertion: Linea aspera of femur (medial lip).

Action: Hip joint: thigh flexion, thigh adduction, thigh external rotation; pelvis stabilization.

Innervation: Obturator nerve (L2-L4).

Blood supply: Arteria profunda femoris.

GRACILIS: (See figure 50)

Origin: Anterior body of pubis, inferior pubic ramus, ischial ramus

Insertion: Medial surface of proximal tibia (via pes anserinus)

Actions: Hip joint: Thigh flexion, thigh adduction; Knee joint: leg flexion, leg internal rotation.

Innervation: Obturator nerve (L2-L3)

Blood supply: Deep femoral artery (via artery to the adductors)

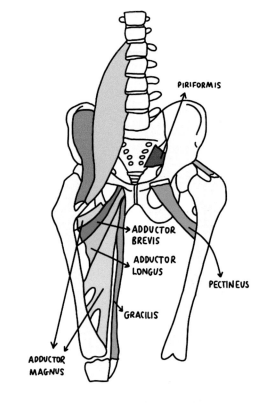

Figure 52. Illustration of the anterior portion of the thigh muscles.

PECTINEUS: See page 105-106.

MUSCLES MEDIALLY ROTATING THE HIP JOINT:

ANTERIOR PART OF GLUTEUS MEDIUS: See page 107-108.

ANTERIOR PART OF GLUTEUS MINIMUS: See page 108.

TENSOR FASCIA LATAE: See page 108.

PSOAS MAJOR: See page 105.

ILIACUS: See page 105.

MUSCLES LATERALLY ROTATING THE HIP JOINT:

GLUTEUS MAXIMUS: See page 106.

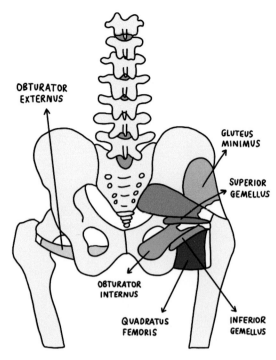

Figure 53. Illustration of the anterior portion of the hip muscles.

PIRIFORMIS: (See figure 51)

Origin: Anterior surface of the sacrum (between the S2 and S4), Gluteal surface of ilium (near posterior inferior iliac spine), (Sacrotuberous ligament).

Insertion: (Apex of) Greater trochanter of the femur.

Action: Hip joint: Thigh external rotation, Thigh abduction (from flexed hip); Stabilizes head of femur in acetabulum.

Innervation: Nerve to piriformis (S1-S2).

Blood supply: Superior gluteal artery, inferior gluteal artery, gemellar branches of the internal pudendal.

OBTURATOR INTERNUS:

Origin: Posterior surface of the obturator membrane; bony boundaries of the obturator foramen.

Insertion: Medial surface of greater trochanter of femur.

Action: External rotation of extended thigh; Abduction of flexed thigh; Stabilization of hip joint.

Innervation: Nerve to obturator internus (L5 and S1).

Blood supply: Obturator artery; internal pudendal artery.

GEMELLUS SUPERIOR:

Origin: Ischial spine.

Insertion: Medial surface of greater trochanter of femur (via tendon of obturator internus).

Action: Hip joint: Thigh external rotation, thigh abduction (from flexed hip); stabilizes head of femur in acetabulum.

Innervation: Nerve to obturator internus (L5-S1).

Blood supply: Internal pudendal artery, inferior gluteal artery (and occasionally superior gluteal artery).

GEMELLUS INFERIOR:

Origin: Ischial tuberosity.

Insertion: Medial surface of greater trochanter of femur (via tendon of obturator internus).

Action: Hip joint: Thigh external rotation, thigh abduction (from flexed hip), stabilizes head of femur in acetabulum.

Innervation: Nerve to quadratus femoris (L4/5, S1).

Blood supply: Medial circumflex femoral artery.

QUADRATUS FEMORIS:

Origin: Ischial tuberosity.

Insertion: Intertrochanteric crest of femur.

Action: Hip joint: thigh external rotation; stabilizes head of femur in acetabulum.

Innervation: Nerve to quadratus femoris (L4-S1).

Blood supply: Inferior gluteal artery.

OBTURATOR EXTERNUS:

Origin: Anterior surface of obturator membrane, bony boundaries of obturator foramen.

Insertion: Trochanteric fossa of femur.

Action: Hip joint: Thigh external rotation, thigh abduction (from flexed hip); Stabilizes head of femur in acetabulum.

Innervation: Obturator nerve (L3, L4).

Blood supply: Obturator and medial circumflex femoral arteries.

QUICK FIRE QUIZ!! (Answers at the back of this book!)

What is the insertion of the obturator internus?

CHAPTER THIRTEEN

THE KNEE

THE BONES OF THE KNEE

On this page we will be taking a look at the bones that make up the knee joint, including the tibia, the femur, the patella, and the fibula.

THE FEMUR: Details are given on page 102.

THE PATELLA:

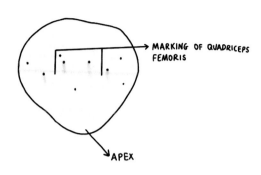

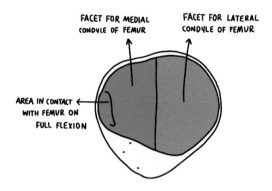

THE TIBIA AND FIBULA:

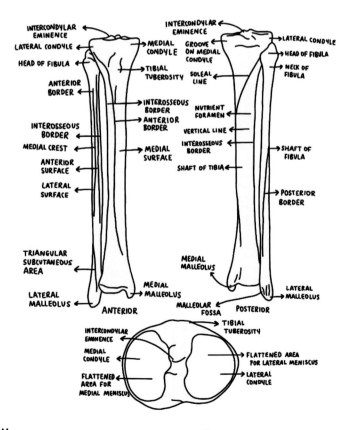

QUICK FIRE QUIZ!! (Answers at the back of this book!)

Can you name a bony landmark on the tibia bone?

THE KNEE JOINT

On this page, we will take a closer look at the knee joint itself. We will examine structures such as the ligaments, blood supply and innervation. There are 2 different joints that make up the knee, the tibiofemoral joint (joint between the tibia and femur) and the patellofemoral joint (the joint between the patella and the femur).

THE TIBIOFEMORAL JOINT AND THE PATELLOFEMORAL JOINT:

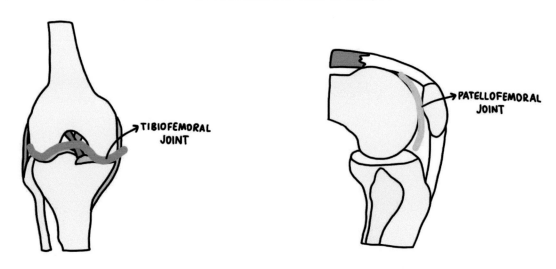

Figure 54. Illustration of the tibiofemoral and patellofemoral joint.

TYPE	Tibiofemoral joint: Synovial hinge joint; uniaxial Patellofemoral joint: Plane joint
ARTICULAR SURFACES	Tibiofemoral joint: lateral and medial condyles of femur, tibial plateaus Patellofemoral joint: patellar surface of femur, posterior surface of patella
LIGAMENTS AND MENISCI	Extracapsular ligaments: patellar ligament, medial and lateral patellar retinacula, tibial (medial) collateral ligament, fibular (lateral) collateral ligament, oblique popliteal ligament, arcuate popliteal ligament, anterolateral ligament (ALL) Intracapsular ligaments: anterior cruciate ligament (ACL), posterior cruciate ligament (PCL), medial meniscus, lateral meniscus
INNERVATION	Femoral nerve (nerve to vastus medialis, saphenous nerve) tibial and common fibular (peroneal) nerves, posterior division of the obturator nerve
BLOOD SUPPLY	Genicular branches of lateral circumflex femoral artery, femoral artery, posterior tibial artery, anterior tibial artery and popliteal artery
MOVEMENTS	Extension, flexion, medial rotation, lateral rotation

QUICK FIRE QUIZ!! (Answers at the back of this book!)

What are the articular surfaces of the patellofemoral joint?

....

THE LIGAMENTS OF THE KNEE

PATELLAR LIGAMENT: This ligament is an extension of the quadriceps tendon. It connects the patella to the top of the tuberosity (a ridge-like prominence) of the tibia, or shinbone.

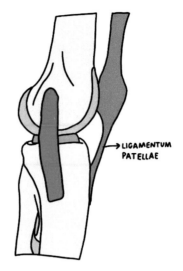

LIGAMENTUM PATELLAE

MEDIAL AND LATERAL PATELLAR RETINACULA: The
medial patellar retinaculum fills in the gap between
the patella, patellar ligament, and medial collateral
ligament to seal the fibrous capsule, whilst the lateral
patellar retinaculum fills the gap on the lateral side
of the patella (including the PCL ligament).

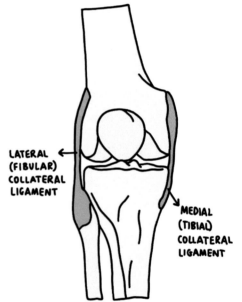

LATERAL (FIBULAR) COLLATERAL LIGAMENT

MEDIAL (TIBIAL) COLLATERAL LIGAMENT

TIBIAL (MEDIAL) COLLATERAL LIGAMENT (MCL):
(Extracapsular and sits medially) The MCL connects the
top of the tibia, or shinbone, to the bottom of the
femur, or thighbone. It also prevents excess valgus
(medial) stress to the knee joint.

FIBULAR (LATERAL) COLLATERAL LIGAMENT
(LCL): (Extracapsular and sits laterally) This
ligament originates on the lateral epicondyle of
the femur and inserts on the fibular head. It also
prevents excess varus (lateral) stress to the knee
joint.

OBLIQUE POPLITEAL LIGAMENT: This ligament
originates as an extension of the semimembranosus
muscle tendon. This ligament also crosses the back
of the knee.

ARCUATE POPLITEAL LIGAMENT: The arcuate
popliteal ligament is an extracapsular ligament of
the knee. It is Y-shaped and is attached to the
posterior portion of the head of the fibula. From
there it goes to its two insertions: medially and laterally.

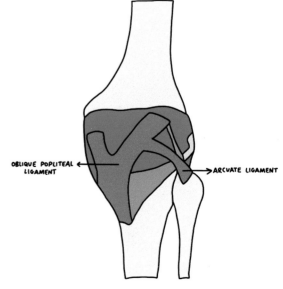

OBLIQUE POPLITEAL LIGAMENT

ARCUATE LIGAMENT

ANTEROLATERAL LIGAMENT (ALL): The anterolateral ligament is a ligament on the lateral aspect of the knee, anterior to the fibular collateral ligament.

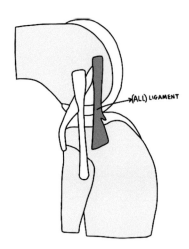

ANTERIOR CRUCIATE LIGAMENT (ACL): This ligament joins your thigh bone (femur) to the front of your shin bone (tibia).

POSTERIOR CRUCIATE LIGAMENT (PCL): The posterior cruciate ligament and ACL connect your thighbone (femur) to your shinbone (tibia).

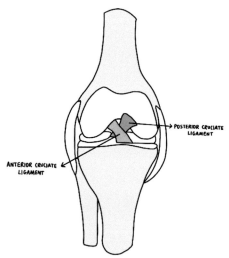

MEDIAL MENISCUS: The medial meniscus is a fibrocartilage semi-circular band that spans the knee joint medially, located between the medial condyle of the femur and the medial condyle of the tibia.

LATERAL MENISCUS: The lateral meniscus is a fibrocartilaginous semi-circular band that spans the lateral side of the interior of the knee joint.

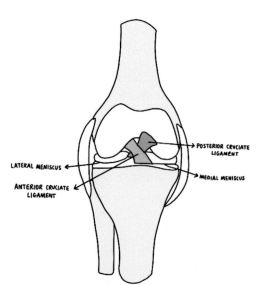

MUSCLES OF THE KNEE JOINT:

MUSCLES FLEXING THE KNEE JOINT:

HAMSTRINGS (SEMITENDINOSUS, SEMIMEMBRANOSUS, AND BICEPS FEMORIS): See page 106-107.

GASTROCNEMIUS:

Origin: Lateral head: Posterolateral aspect of lateral condyle of the femur. Medial head: Posterior surface of medial femoral condyle, popliteal surface of femoral shaft.

Insertion: Posterior surface of the calcaneus via the calcaneal tendon.

Innervation: Tibial nerve (S1, S2).

Function: Talocrural joint: Foot plantar flexion.

Knee joint: Leg flexion.

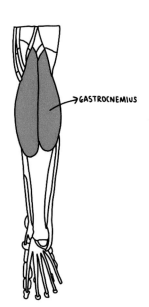

GRACILIS: See page 109.

SARTORIUS: See page 106.

POPLITEUS:

Origin: Lateral condyle of femur, posterior horn of lateral meniscus of knee joint.

Insertion: Posterior surface of proximal tibia.

Innervation: Tibial nerve (L4-S1).

Blood supply: Inferior medial and lateral genicular arteries (popliteal artery), posterior tibial recurrent artery, posterior tibial artery, nutrient artery of tibia.

Function: Unlocks knee joint; Knee joint stabilization.

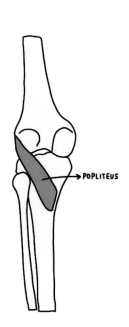

MUSCLES EXTENDING THE KNEE JOINT:

QUADRICEPS FEMORIS:

Parts: Rectus femoris, vastus lateralis, vastus medialis, vastus intermedius.

Origins: Rectus femoris: Anterior inferior iliac spine, supraacetabular groove. Vastus medialis: Intertrochanteric line, pectineal line of femur, linea aspera, medial supracondylar line of femur. Vastus lateralis: Intertrochanteric line, greater trochanter, gluteal tuberosity, linea aspera of femur. Vastus intermedius: Anterior surface of femoral shaft.

Insertions: Rectus femoris and vastus intermedius: Tibial tuberosity (via patellar ligament), patella. Vastus lateralis: Tibial tuberosity (via patellar ligament), patella, (lateral condyle of tibia). Vastus medialis: Tibial tuberosity (via patellar ligament), patella, (medial condyle of tibia).

Innervation: Femoral nerve (L2–L4).

Function: Hip joint: Thigh flexion (rectus femoris only).

Knee joint: Leg extension.

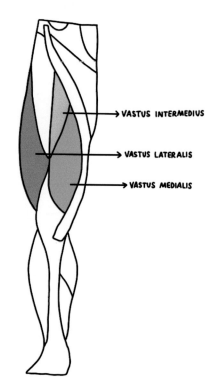

RECTUS FEMORIS: See Page 106.

VASTUS LATERALIS: See Quadriceps Femoris above.

VASTUS MEDIALIS: See Quadriceps Femoris above.

VASTUS INTERMEDIUS: See Quadriceps Femoris above.

TENSOR FASCIA LATAE: See page 108.

MUSCLES LATERALLY ROTATING THE TIBIA AT THE KNEE JOINT:

BICEPS FEMORIS: See page 107.

MUSCLES MEDIALLY ROTATING THE TIBIA AT THE KNEE JOINT:

SEMITENDINOSUS: See page 106–107.

SEMIMEMBRANOSUS: See page 107.

GRACILIS: See page 109.

SARTORIUS: See page 106.

POPLITEUS: See page 117.

CHAPTER FOURTEEN

THE LEG/CALF

BONES OF THE LEG/CALF

We already covered the tibia and fibula (which are the 2 bones present in the lower leg) over on pages (enter no.) so if you need a recap head on over there!

JOINTS OF THE LEG/CALF

Now that we have covered the bones of the leg, we shall take a look at the joints present.

SUPERIOR TIBIOFIBULAR JOINT:

Articular surfaces: Lateral tibial condyle, head of fibula.

Ligaments: Anterior ligament of fibular head, posterior ligament of fibular head.

Innervation: Common fibular nerve, nerve to popliteus.

Blood supply: Anterior and posterior tibial recurrent arteries.

Movements: Slight gliding following the ankle joint movements.

INFERIOR TIBIOFIBULAR JOINT:

Articular surfaces: Distal end of fibula, fibular notch of tibia.

Ligaments: Anterior, interosseous, posterior, and transverse tibiofibular ligaments.

Innervation: Deep fibular and sural nerves.

Blood supply: Fibular artery, lateral malleolar branches.

Movements: Slight gliding following the ankle joint movements.

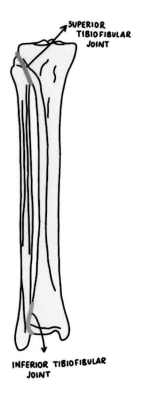

Figure 55. Illustration of the joints within the lower leg.

LIGAMENTS OF THE CALF/ LEG

ANTERIOR LIGAMENT OF FIBULAR HEAD: The anterior ligament of the head of the fibula consists of two or three broad and flat bands, which pass obliquely upward from the front of the head of the fibula to the front of the lateral condyle of the tibia.

POSTERIOR LIGAMENT OF FIBULAR HEAD: The posterior ligament of the head of the fibula is a part of the knee. It is a single thick and broad band, which passes obliquely upward from the back of the head of the fibula to the back of the lateral condyle of the tibia.

INTEROSSEOUS LIGAMENT OF FIBULAR HEAD: The interosseous tibiofibular ligament connects the facing surfaces of the bones and it is continuous with the interosseous membrane of the leg. It strongly connects the bones and it is the principal stabilizer of this joint.

QUICK FIRE QUIZ!! (Answers at the back of book!)

Can you describe the position of the posterior ligament of the fibular head?

....

CHAPTER FIFTEEN

THE ANKLE

THE ANKLE BONES

On this page we will be discussing the ankle bones. The ankle joint is a synovial joint with one degree of freedom allowing for plantarflexion and dorsiflexion.

THE TIBIA AND FIBULA: Details of these bones are given on page 113.

TALUS BONE:

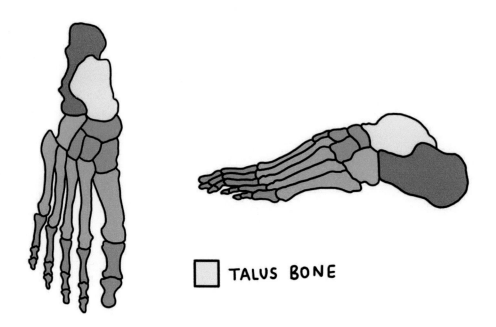

☐ TALUS BONE

Figure 56. Illustration of the location of the talus bone in the foot / ankle.

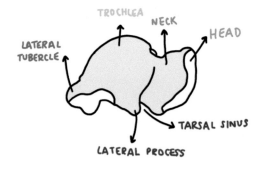

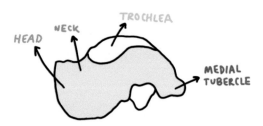

Figure 57. Illustration of the talus bone in the foot / ankle.

QUICK FIRE QUIZ!! (Answers at the back of this book!)

Can you name any bony landmarks of the talus bone?

....

THE ANKLE JOINT

Now we have looked at the bones of the ankle, we will take a closer look at the ankle joint itself.

THE TALOCURAL JOINT:

TYPE	Synovial hinge joint; uniaxial
ARTICULAR SURFACES	Tibiotarsal joint: distal end of tibia, medial malleolus of the tibia, lateral malleolus of fibula, body of talus
LIGAMENTS	Anterior talofibular, posterior talofibular, calcaneofibular, deltoid (tibiocalcaneal, tibionavicular, tibiotalar parts), fibular collateral ligaments
INNERVATION	Deep fibular (peroneal), tibial and sural nerves
BLOOD SUPPLY	Anterior tibial, posterior tibial and fibular arteries
MOVEMENTS	Dorsiflexion, plantar flexion

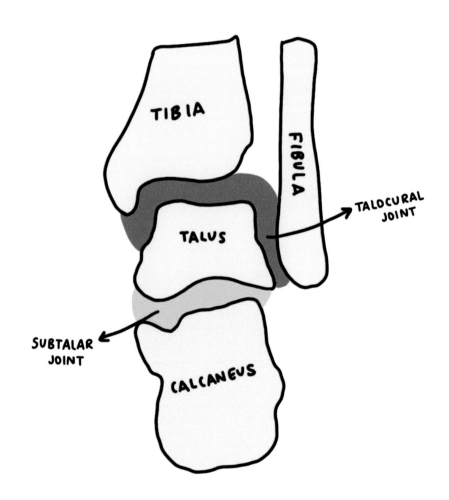

Figure 58. Illustration of the Talocrural joint in the ankle and the subtalar joint which will be looked at in more detail in the foot chapter.

QUICK FIRE QUIZ!! (Answers at the back of this book!)

What is the blood supply for the talocrural joint?

....

LIGAMENTS OF THE ANKLE

ANTERIOR TALOFIBULAR LIGAMENT: The anterior talofibular ligament is a ligament in the ankle. It passes from the anterior margin of the fibular malleolus, anteriorly and laterally, to the talus bone, in front of its lateral articular facet.

POSTERIOR TALOFIBULAR LIGAMENT: This is a ligament that connects the fibula to the talus bone.

CALCANEOFIBULAR LIGAMENT: This ligament joins the calcaneus to the fibula.

LATERAL COLLATERAL LIGAMENT COMPLEX: The lateral collateral ligament (complex) of the ankle is a set of three ligaments that resist inversion of the ankle joint. They are more commonly injured than the medial collateral (deltoid) ligament of the ankle. They run from the lateral malleolus of the fibula to the talus and calcaneus. This complex is made up of the ATFL (anterior talofibular ligament), the PTFL (posterior talofibular ligament), and the Calcaneofibular ligament.

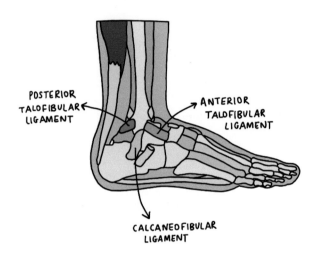

DELTOID (TIBIOCALCANEAL, TIBIONAVICULAR, TIBIOTALAR PARTS) LIGAMENT: The deltoid ligament is a strong, flat, triangular band, attached, above, to the apex and anterior and posterior borders of the medial malleolus. The deltoid ligament is composed of: 1. Anterior tibiotalar ligament 2. Tibiocalcaneal ligament 3. Posterior tibiotalar ligament 4. Tibionavicular ligament. These ligaments sit medially on the ankle.

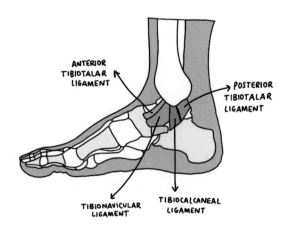

QUICK FIRE QUIZ!! (Answers at the back of this book!)

Can you describe the difference between the lateral collateral ligament complex and the deltoid ligament?

THE MUSCLES OF THE ANKLE JOINT

Now we have looked at the bones, the joint, and the ligaments of the ankle joint, let us take a closer look at the muscles.

MUSCLES PLANTARFLEXING THE ANKLE JOINT:

GASTROCNEMIUS: (See page (enter no.))

SOLEUS:

Origin: Soleal line, medial border of tibia, head of fibula, posterior border of fibula.

Insertion: Posterior surface of calcaneus (via calcaneal tendon).

Innervation: Tibial nerve (S1, S2).

Vascularization: Posterior tibial artery and vein.

Function: Talocrural joint: Foot plantar flexion.

Clinical relations: Soleus tear, soleus pain.

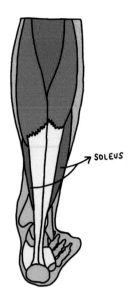

PLANTARIS:

Origin: Lateral supracondylar line of femur, oblique popliteal ligament of knee.

Insertion: Posterior surface of calcaneus (via calcaneal tendon).

Action: Talocrural joint: foot plantar flexion. Knee joint: knee flexion.

Innervation: Tibial nerve (S1, S2).

Blood supply: Superficially: lateral sural and popliteal arteries. Deeply: superior lateral genicular artery.

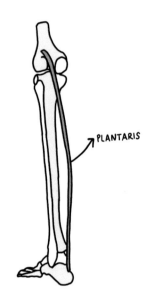

FIBIULARIS (PERONEUS) LONGUS:

Origin: Head of fibula, proximal 2/3 of lateral surface of fibula, intermuscular septa.

Insertion: Medial cuneiform bone, metatarsal bone 1.

Action: Talocrural joint: Foot plantar flexion; Subtalar joint: Foot eversion; Supports longitudinal and transverse arches of foot.

Innervation: Superficial fibular nerve (L5, S1).

Blood supply: Fibular artery.

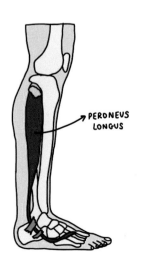

FIBULARIS (PERONEUS) BREVIS:

Origin: Distal 2/3 of the lateral surface of fibula, anterior inermuscular septum.

Insertion: Tuberosity of the 5th metatarsal bone.

Action: Talocrural joint: Foot plantar flexion. Subtalar joint: Foot eversion.

Innervation: Superficial fibular nerve (L5, S1).

Blood supply: Anterior tibial artery.

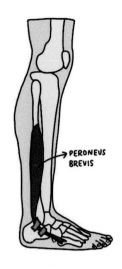

TIBIALIS POSTERIOR:

Origin: Posterior surface of tibia, posterior surface of fibula and interosseous membrane.

Insertion: Tuberosity of navicular bone, all cuneiform bones, cuboid bone, bases of metatarsal bones 2-4.

Actions: Talocrural joint: Foot plantarflexion. Subtalar joint: Foot inversion. Supports medial longitudinal arch of foot.

Innervation: Tibial nerve (L4, L5).

Blood supply: Branches of the posterior tibial artery.

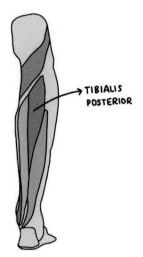

FLEXOR DIGITORUM LONGUS:

Origin: Posterior surface of tibia (inferior to soleal line).

Insertion: Bases of distal phalanges of digits 2-5.

Action: Metatarsophalangeal and interphalangeal joints 2-5: toe flexion. Talocrural joint: foot plantar flexion. Subtalar joint: foot inversion.

Innervation: Tibial nerve (L5, S1, S2).

Blood supply: Posterior tibial artery.

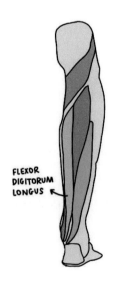

FLEXOR HALLUCIS LONGUS:

Origin: (Distal 2/3 of) Posterior surface of fibula, interosseous membrane, posterior intermuscular septum of leg, fascia of tibialis posterior muscle.

Insertion: Base of distal phalanx of great toe.

Innervation: Tibial nerve (S2, S3).

Function: Metatarsophalangeal and interphalangeal joint 1: Toe flexion; Talocrural joint: Foot plantar flexion; Subtalar joint: Foot inversion.

Blood supply: Posterior tibial artery, fibular artery.

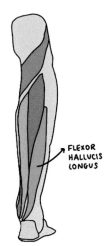

FLEXOR HALLUCIS LONGUS

MUSCLES DORSIFLEXING THE ANKLE JOINT:

TIBIALIS ANTERIOR:

Origin: Lateral surface of tibia, interosseous membrane.

Insertion: Medial cuneiform bone, base of metatarsal bone 1.

Action: Talocrural joint: foot dorsiflexion; subtalar joint: foot inversion.

Innervation: Deep fibular nerve (L4, L5).

Blood supply: Branches of anterior tibial artery: Anterior and medial muscular branches; anterior tibial recurrent, dorsalis pedis and anterior medial malleolar arteries. Branches of posterior tibial artery: Medial malleolar and calcaneal arteries.

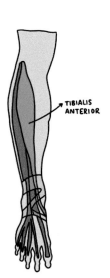

TIBIALIS ANTERIOR

EXTENSOR DIGITORUM LONGUS:

Origin: (Proximal half of) medial surface of fibula, lateral tibial condyle, interosseus membrane.

Insertion: Distal and middle phalanges of digits 2-5.

Action: Metatarsophalangeal and interphalangeal joints 2-5: Toe extension; Talocrural joint: Foot dorsiflexion; Subtalar joint: Foot eversion.

Innervation: Deep fibular nerve (L5, S1).

Blood supply: Anterior tibial, fibular, anterior lateral malleolar, lateral tarsal, metatarsal, plantar, and digital arteries.

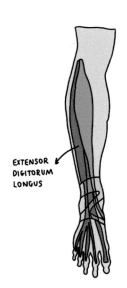

EXTENSOR DIGITORUM LONGUS

EXTENSOR HALLUCIS LONGUS:

Origin: Middle third of medial surface of fibula, interosseous membrane.

Insertion: Base of distal phalanx of great toe.

Action: Metatarsophalangeal and interphalangeal joint 1: toe extension; talocrural joint: foot dorsiflexion.

127

Innervation: Deep fibular nerve (L5, S1).

Blood supply: Anterior tibial artery.

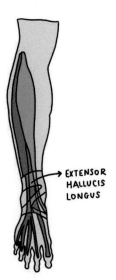

EXTENSOR
HALLUCIS
LONGUS

FIBULARIS TERTIUS:

Origin: Medial surface (distal third) of fibula, interosseous membrane (anterior surface), anterior intermuscular septum.

Insertion: Dorsal surface of base of metatarsal bone 5.

Action: Talocrural joint: Foot dorsiflexion. Subtalar joint: Foot eversion.

Innervation: Deep fibular nerve (L5, S1).

Blood supply: Anterior lateral malleolar artery, lateral tarsal artery, metatarsal arteries, lateral plantar artery, digita

l arteries, arcuate artery, fourth dorsal metatarsal artery.

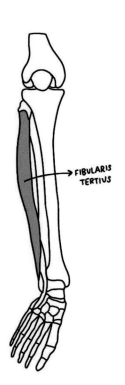

FIBULARIS
TERTIUS

QUICK FIRE QUIZ!! (Answers at the back of book!)

What is the insertion of the peroneus longus?

....

....

CHAPTER SIXTEEN

THE FOOT

THE FOOT BONES

Now we have looked at the ankle in more detail, let us take a closer look at the bones of the foot.

TARSAL BONES, METATARSAL BONES, AND PHALANGES:

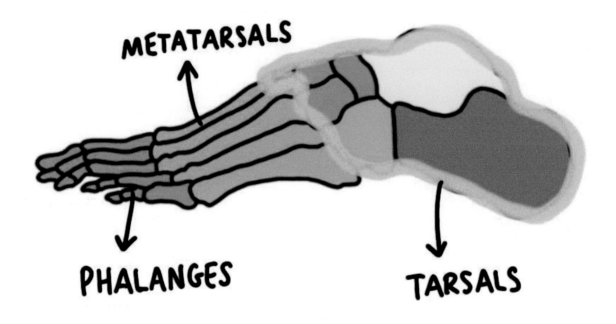

Figure 59. Illustration of the tarsal bones, metatarsals, and phalanges.

QUICK FIRE QUIZ!! (Answers are at the back of book!)

Name 3 bones present in the foot.

....

JOINTS OF THE FOOT

Now we have looked at the bones a little more closely, let us take a look at the joints of the foot.

INTERTARSAL:

The intertarsal joints are between the tarsal bones. These joints are the subtalar (talocalcaneal), talocalcaneonavicular, calcaneocuboid, cuneonavicular, cuboideonavicular, and Intercuneiform joints.

TARSOMETATARSAL AND INTERMETATARSAL:

Tarsometatarsal joints are the movements between the tarsals and metatarsals.

METATARSOPHALANGEAL:

Metatarsophalangeal joints (MTP) are the joints between the heads of metatarsals and corresponding bases of the proximal phalanges of the foot.

INTERPHALANGEAL:

Interphalangeal joints are between the phalanges of the foot. The great toe has only one interphalangeal joint, while the other four toes have a proximal (PIP) and a distal (DIP) interphalangeal joint.

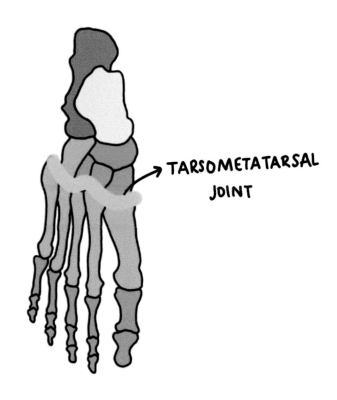

TARSOMETATARSAL JOINT

Figure 60. Illustration of the Tarsometatarsal joint.

TYPE	Hinge joints; uniaxial
ARTICULAR SURFACES	Proximal interphalangeal joints: head of proximal phalanx, base of middle phalanx; Distal interphalangeal joints: head of middle phalanx, base of distal phalanx; Interphalangeal joint of big toe: head of proximal phalanx, base of distal phalanx;
LIGAMENTS	Collateral ligaments, plantar ligament
INNERVATION	Dorsal digital and proper plantar nerves (of medial and lateral plantar nerve)
BLOOD SUPPLY	Digital branches of plantar arch
MOVEMENTS	Flexion, extension

QUICK FIRE QUIZ!! (Answers at the back of book!)

What is the blood supply for the interphalangeal joint?

....

THE LIGAMENTS OF THE FOOT

INTEROSSEOUS (TALOCALCANEAN) LIGAMENT: This ligament forms a bond between the talus and calcaneus.

MEDIAL TALOCALCANEAN LIGAMENT: This ligament connects the talus and the calcaneus medially.

POSTERIOR TALOCALCANEAN LIGAMENT: This ligament connects the talus and the calcaneus posteriorly.

LATERAL TALOCALCANEAN LIGAMENT: This ligament connects the talus and the calcaneus laterally.

LIGAMENTUM CERVICIS: At the lateral end of the sinus tarsi (a small tunnel that sits between the 2 parts of the subtalar joint in the ankle) is this ligament which attaches to the neck of the talus above and the calcaneus below.

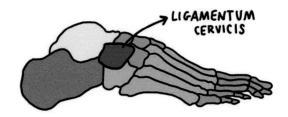

PLANTAR CALCANEONAVICULAR LIGAMENT: This ligament sits on the plantar surface of the foot and connects the navicular bone to the calcaneus bone.

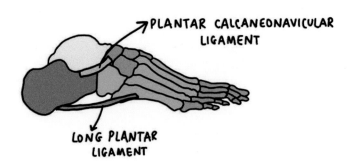

DORSAL TALONAVICULAR LIGAMENT: This ligament connects the neck of the talus to the dorsal surface of the navicular bone.

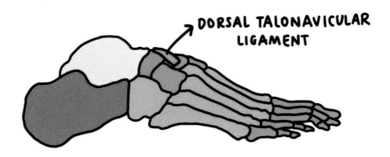

DORSAL TALONAVICULAR LIGAMENT

BIFURCATE LIGAMENT: The bifurcate ligament is a strong band, attached behind to the deep hollow on the upper surface of the calcaneus and dividing in front in a Y-shaped manner into a calcaneocuboid and a calcaneonavicular part.

DORSAL CALCANEOCUBOID LIGAMENT: This ligament extends from the heel bone to the cuboid tarsal bone dorsally.

PLANTAR CALCANEOCUBOID LIGAMENT: A ligament on the bottom of the foot that connects the calcaneus to the cuboid bone.

INTEROSSEOUS CUNEOCUBOID LIGAMENT: This ligament consists of a series of fibrous bands that connect the central portion of the cuboid to the lateral surfaces of the cuneiform bones.

LONG PLANTAR LIGAMENT: The long plantar ligament extends from the calcaneus (heel bone) to the cuboid bone, which is on the outside of the foot.

DORSAL TARSOMETATARSAL LIGAMENT: This ligament connects the metatarsal bones with the cuneiform and cuboid bones dorsally.

PLANTAR TARSOMETATARSAL LIGAMENT: This ligament connects the metatarsal bones with the cuneiform and cuboid bones on the plantar surface.

INTEROSSEOUS TARSOMETATARSAL LIGAMENT: The three interosseous tarsometatarsal ligaments are located in the cuneometatarsal joint spaces. This ligament also connects the metatarsal bones with the cuneiform and cuboid bones.

COLLATERAL LIGAMENTS: The collateral ligaments of the interphalangeal joints of the foot are fibrous bands that are situated on both sides of the interphalangeal joints of the toes.

DEEP TRANSVERSE METATARSAL LIGAMENT: The transverse metatarsal ligament is a narrow band which runs across and connects together the heads of all the metatarsal bones.

QUICK FIRE QUIZ!! (Answers at the back of book!)

What is the location of the dorsal talonavicular ligament?

....

THE MUSCLES OF THE FOOT

MUSCLES INVERTING THE FOOT:

TIBIALIS POSTERIOR: See page 126.

TIBIALIS ANTERIOR: See page 127.

MUSCLES EVERTING THE FOOT:

FIBULARIS (PERONEUS) LONGUS: See page 125.

FIBULARIS (PERONEUS) BREVIS: See page 126.

FIBULARIS (PERONEUS) TERTIUS: See page 128.

MUSCLES EXTENDING THE TOES:

EXTENSOR HALLUCIS LONGUS: See page 127-128.

EXTENSOR DIGITORUM LONGUS: See page 127.

EXTENSOR DIGITORUM BREVIS:

Origin: Superolateral surface of calcaneus bone, interosseous talocalcaneal ligament; stem of inferior extensor retinaculum.

Insertion: Extensor digitorum longus tendons of toes 2—4.

Action: Distal interphalangeal joints 2-4: Toe extension.

Innervation: Deep fibular/peroneal nerve (L5, S1).

Blood supply: Fibular artery, anterior tibial artery, dorsalis pedis artery.

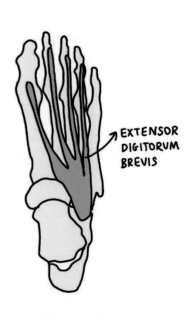

EXTENSOR DIGITORUM BREVIS

LUMBRICALS:

Origin: Tendons of flexor digitorum longus.

Insertion: Medial bases of proximal phalanges and extensor expansion of digits 2-5.

Function: Metatarsophalangeal joints 2-5: Toe flexion, Toes adduction; Interphalangeal joints 2-5: Toes extension.

Innervation: Lumbrical 1: Medial plantar nerve (S2,S3); Lumbricals 2-4: Lateral plantar nerve (S2-S3).

Blood supply: Lateral plantar artery, plantar metatarsal arteries, dorsal metatarsal arteries, dorsal digital arteries.

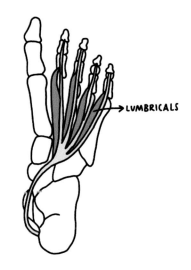

MUSCLES FLEXING THE TOES:

FLEXOR DIGITORUM LONGUS: See page 126.

FLEXOR ACCESSORIES (QUADRATUS PLANTAE):

Origin: Medial surface of calcaneus bone, lateral process of calcaneal tuberosity.

Insertion: Tendon of flexor digitorum longus.

Action: Metatarsophalangeal joints 2-5: Toe flexion.

Innervation: Lateral plantar nerve (S1-S3).

Blood supply: Medial plantar artery, lateral plantar artery, deep plantar arterial arch.

FLEXOR DIGITORUM BREVIS:

Origin: Medial process of calcaneal tuberosity, plantar aponeurosis and intermuscular septum.

Insertion: Middle phalanges of digits 2-5.

Action: Metatarsophalangeal joints 2-5: Toe flexion; supports longitudinal arch of foot.

Innervation: Medial plantar nerve (S1-S3).

Blood supply: Medial and lateral plantar arteries and plantar arch, plantar metatarsal and plantar digital arteries.

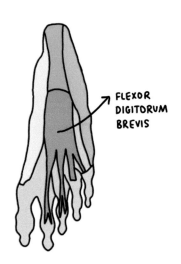

FLEXOR HALLUCIS LONGUS: See Page 126-127.

FLEXOR HALLUCIS BREVIS:

Origin: Tendon of tibialis posterior, medial cuneiform bone, lateral cuneiform bone, cuboid bone.

Insertion: Lateral and medial aspects of base of proximal phalanx of great toe.

135

Action: Metatarsophalangeal joint 1: Toe flexion; Support of longitudinal arch of foot.

Innervation: Medial plantar nerve (S1, S2).

Blood supply: First metatarsal artery (plantar arch); superficial branch of the medial plantar artery (posterior tibial artery).

FLEXOR DIGITI MINIMI BREVIS:

Origin: Base of metatarsal bone 5, long plantar ligament.

Insertion: Base of proximal phalanx of digit 5.

Action: Metatarsophalangeal joint 5: Toe flexion.

Innervation: Lateral plantar nerve (S2 — S3).

Blood supply: Arcuate, lateral tarsal and lateral plantar arteries.

PLANTAR INTEROSSEI:

Origin: Medial aspects of metatarsal bones 3-5.

Insertion: Medial bases of proximal phalanges and extensor expansion of digits 3-5.

Action: Metatarsophalangeal joints 3-5: Toe flexion, toes adduction; Interphalangeal joints 3-5: Toes extension.

Innervation: Lateral plantar nerve (S2-S3).

Blood supply: Lateral plantar artery.

LUMBRICALS: See Page 135.

<u>MUSCLES ABDUCTING THE TOES:</u>
ABDUCTOR HALLUCIS:

Origin: Medial process of calcaneal tuberosity, flexor retinaculum, plantar aponeurosis.

Insertion: Base of proximal phalanx of great toe.

Action: Metatarsophalangeal joint 1: Toe abduction, toe flexion; Support of longitudinal arch of foot.

Innervation: Medial plantar nerve (S1-S3).

Blood supply: Medial plantar and first plantar metatarsal arteries.

ABDUCTOR DIGITI MINIMI:

Origin: Calcaneal tuberosity, plantar aponeurosis.

Insertion: Base of proximal phalanx of digit 5, metatarsal bone 5.

Action: Metatarsophalangeal joint 5: Toe abduction, toe flexion; Supports longitudinal arch of foot.

Innervation: Lateral plantar nerve (S1-S3).

Blood supply: Lateral plantar artery.

DORSAL INTEROSSEI:

Origin: Opposing sides of metatarsal bones 1-5.

Insertion 1: Medial base of proximal phalanx of digit. 2-4: Lateral bases of proximal phalanges and extensor expansion of digits 2-4.

Action: Metatarsophalangeal joints 2-4: toe flexion, toe abduction; Interphalangeal joints 2-4: toe extension.

Innervation: Lateral plantar nerve (S2-S3).

Blood supply: Arcuate artery, dorsal and plantar metatarsal arteries.

MUSCLES ADDUCTING THE TOES:

ADDUCTOR HALLUCIS:

Origin: Oblique head: bases of metatarsal bones 2-4, cuboid bone, lateral cuneiform bone, tendon of fibularis longus. Transverse head: plantar metatarsophalangeal ligaments of toes 3-5, deep transverse metatarsal ligaments of toes 3-5.

Insertion: Lateral aspect of base of proximal phalanx of great toe.

Action: Metatarsophalangeal joint 1: Toe adduction, toe flexion; Support of longitudinal and transverse arches of foot.

Innervation: Lateral plantar nerve (S2,S3).

Blood supply: Medial plantar artery, lateral plantar artery, plantar arch, plantar metatarsal arteries.

PLANTAR INTEROSSEI: See page 136.

CHAPTER
SEVENTEEN

THE NERVES OF THE LOWER LIMB

THE LOWER LIMB NERVES (THE LUMBAR, LUMBOSACRAL AND SACRAL PLEXUSES)

LUMBAR PLEXUS:

Function: Innervation of the lower anterior abdominal wall and certain muscles of the thigh.

Source: L1 - L4.

Branches: Iliohypogastric and ilioinguinal (L1) - transversus abdominis, internal oblique muscles. Genitofemoral (L1, L2) - cremaster muscle. Lateral femoral cutaneous (L2, L3) - skin of the lateral part of the thigh. Obturator (L2, L3, L4) - obturator externus, adductor longus, adductor brevis, gracilis, pectineus, adductor magnus. Femoral (L2, L3, L4) - Iliopsoas, pectineus, sartorius, quadriceps femoris.

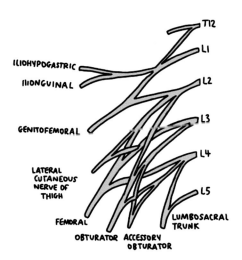

ILIOHYPOGASTRIC NERVE:

Origin: Lumbar plexus (L1).

Branches: Anterior cutaneous branch, lateral cutaneous branch.

Innervation: Motor: Transversus abdominis, internal abdominal oblique, conjoint tendon. Sensory: External abdominal oblique, transversus abdominis, internal abdominal oblique; Skin of the suprapubic region and posterolateral aspect of gluteal region.

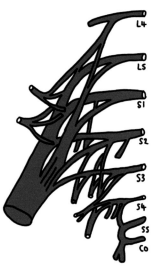

Figure 61. Illustration of the Lumbar and Lumbosacral plexus.

ILIOINGUINAL NERVE:

Origin: Anterior divisions of L1-L4 spinal nerves.

Course: Upper lateral border of psoas major, then crosses quadratus lumborum and iliacus muscles, then enters transversus abdominis and internal oblique muscles, then reaches spermatic cord.

Functions: Sensory: Sensation to transversus abdominis and internal oblique muscles, anteromedial aspect of the thigh, skin over parts of the external genitalia. Motor: Actions of the transversus abdominis and internal oblique muscles.

Clinical points: Ilioinguinal nerve injury, entrapment, and blocks.

LATERAL CUTANEOUS NERVE OF THIGH:

The peritoneum of the iliac fossa, iliac fascia and the lateral side of the thigh (along the iliotibial tract) to the knee is supplied by an entirely sensory nerve called the lateral cutaneous femoral nerve. Proximally, the nerve is formed by fibers of the posterior division of L2 — L3. It then travels inferolaterally to enter the iliac fossa.

GENITOFEMORAL NERVE:

The genitofemoral nerve is formed by neuronal fibers from L1 — L2 spinal segments. As the name suggests, the nerve splits to supply their respective segments. Fibers of the genital portion arise from L2 and innervate the region of the external and internal spermatic fasciae, as well as tunica vaginalis. Motor innervation is provided for the cremaster muscle and cutaneous supply to the anterior scrotal and labial skin.

The L1 fibers form the femoral component and provides cutaneous innervation at the midinferior point above the inguinal ligament. The genitofemoral nerve also gives a motor branch to the upper part of psoas minor.

OBTURATOR NERVE:

The anterior lumbar outflow from L2, L3 and L4 unite at the level of the iliosacral joint, medial to psoas major, to form the obturator nerve. It passes along the posterior wall of the pelvic cavity; then at the point of bifurcation of the common iliac vessels, it travels toward the obturator foramen where it supplies the pelvic parietal peritoneum.

The nerve then divides into an anterior and a posterior division after coursing through the obturator foramen. The former gives motor supply to adductor brevis, adductor longus, gracilis, occasionally pectineus, and the hip joint and cutaneous supply to the medial side of the thigh. The latter gives motor innervation to obturator externus and the pubic division of adductor magnus, in addition to a thin branch that supplies the knee joint.

Occasionally, nerve fibers of the anterior division of L3 and L4 merge at the iliosacral joint (lateral to the obturator nerve) to form the accessory obturator nerve. It travels anteroinferiorly, deep to the inguinal ligament (over the superior pubic ramus) to supply pectineus.

There is also an accessory obturator nerve.

FEMORAL NERVE:

The femoral nerve is formed from the posterior division of L2, L3 and L4. It gives two cutaneous branches to the iliopsoas muscles; one immediately after the nerve fibers of L2 and L3 meet at about the level of the transverse process of L4, and the other as it courses along the medial surface of the ilium.

The nerve continues its inferior course deep to the lateral part of the inguinal ligament and enters the femoral canal lateral to the femoral vessels. As it enters the canal, it supplies pectineus, and then divides into multiple parts. The branches of the femoral nerve are mostly named for the muscles they innervate. These include:

- The nerve to pectineus
- Two nerves to rectus femoris (one of which also innervates the hip)
- A nerve to vastus lateralis, vastus intermedius, and vastus medius
- Two nerves to sartorius, one of which becomes the intermediate femoral cutaneous nerve and the other, the medial femoral cutaneous nerve. The former gives cutaneous innervation to the fascia lata covering the anterior thigh to the knee as well as the skin in this region. The latter innervates the medial aspect of the thigh.

- The saphenous nerve, which is responsible for giving cutaneous supply to the skin of the anteromedial part of the knee, over the medial malleolus and all the way down to the distal end of the first metatarsal bone.

SAPHENOUS NERVE:

The saphenous nerve (long or internal saphenous nerve) is the largest cutaneous branch of the femoral nerve. It is a strictly sensory nerve, and has no motor function.

LUMBOSACRAL PLEXUS:

The anterior divisions of the lumbar nerves, sacral nerves, and coccygeal nerve form the lumbosacral plexus, the first lumbar nerve being frequently joined by a branch from the twelfth thoracic. Injuries to the lumbosacral plexus are predominantly witnessed as bone injuries. Lumbosacral trunk and sacral plexus palsies are common injury patterns.

SUPERIOR GLUTEAL NERVE:

The superior gluteal nerve is formed from the posterior divisions of the anterior rami of L4, L5, and S1 spinal nerves. It gains access to the gluteal region by coursing over the superior border of piriformis muscle through the greater sciatic foramen. Afterwards, the superior gluteal nerve travels laterally underneath the gluteus medius and innervates the tensor fasciae latae, gluteus medius and gluteus minimus.

INFERIOR GLUTEAL NERVE:

The inferior gluteal nerve receives contributions from the posterior divisions of the anterior rami of the L5, S1, and S2 spinal nerves. It takes a similar route through the greater sciatic foramen, but inferior to piriformis muscle. It travels superficial to the sciatic nerve and innervates the gluteus maximus muscle.

NERVE TO PIRIFORMIS:

The third branch to be formed purely from posterior divisions of anterior rami is the nerve to piriformis. It specifically receives contributions from the posterior divisions of the anterior rami of the S1 and S2 spinal nerves. These nerve fibers have a short course posteriorly and innervate the piriformis muscle.

PERFORATING CUTANEOUS NERVE:

The perforating cutaneous nerve is also formed of purely posterior divisions, this time originating from the fibers of the anterior rami of spinal nerves S2 and S3. It passes through the greater sciatic foramen, superior to the gemelli and obturator internus, piercing the sacrotuberous ligament and gluteus maximus. This nerve provides cutaneous supply to a small area of skin on the inferior medial part of the buttock.

NERVE TO QUADRATUS FEMORIS:

The nerve to quadratus femoris originates from the anterior divisions of the anterior rami of the spinal nerves L4, L5 and S1. The nerve travels inferiorly underneath the sciatic nerve and passes towards the quadratus femoris. Along its course, it supplies the inferior gemellus muscle and provides an articular branch to the hip joint.

NERVE TO OBTURATOR INTERNUS:

The nerve to obturator internus arises from the anterior divisions of the anterior rami of spinal nerves L5, S1 and S2. The nerve travels inferior to piriformis leabes the pelvis through the greater sciatic foramen, where it gives off a branch to innervate the superior gemellus muscle. It then courses around the ischial spine and reenters the pelvis through the lesser sciatic foramen and pierces obturator internus.

PUDENDAL NERVE:

The anterior divisions of the anterior rami of spinal nerve S2, S3 and S4 merge on the anterior surface of piriformis (posterior to the inferior gluteal artery) to form the pudendal nerve. The pudendal nerve travels inferiorly around the sacrospinous ligament to enter the pudendal canal with the pudendal vessels. The pudendal nerve gives rise to:

- The inferior rectal nerve that innervates the external anal sphincter, anal canal and perianal skin.
- The perineal nerve that provides cutaneous supply to part of the posterior scrotum (vulva), mucus membrane of the urethra and vagina, and motor innervation to the muscles of the perineum.
- The dorsal nerve of the clitoris/penis that provides cutaneous innervation to this region.

SCIATIC NERVE:

The sciatic nerve is the terminal and largest branch of the sacral plexus formed from both anterior and posterior divisions of the anterior rami of spinal nerves L4 to S3.

The nerve exits the pelvic cavity by way of the greater sciatic foramen. In the gluteal region, it travels deep to gluteus maximus and the inferior gluteal artery. It courses over the posterior surface of the gemelli, piriformis, quadratus femoris and the ischial fibers of adductor femoris. The sciatic nerve begins branching at about the midpoint between the ischial tuberosity and the greater trochanter to supply the hamstring muscles and the ischial fibers of adductor magnus.

At the apex of the popliteal fossa, the nerve typically divides into the common peroneal and tibial nerves. These two nerves are responsible for innervating the muscles and joints of the leg and foot. It is noteworthy that the sciatic nerve receives vasa nervorum (small artery providing arterial blood to peripheral nerves) from the inferior gluteal artery.

TIBIAL NERVE:

Origin: Sciatic nerve (L4-S3)

Branches: Leg: Muscular branches, articular branches, the sural nerve, medial calcaneal nerve. Foot: Medial plantar nerve, lateral plantar nerve.

Supply: Motor: Posterior compartment of the leg, all intrinsic muscles (except extensor digitorum brevis). Sensory: Skin of the posterolateral leg (the sural nerve), lateral foot and the sole of the foot.

MEDIAL PLANTAR NERVE:

The medial plantar nerve runs deep to the abductor hallucis muscle. Distally, it gives rise to the medial proper digital nerve to the great toe and terminates near the metatarsal bases as three common plantar digital nerves, which further divide into proper plantar digital nerves to toes I-IV. The medial plantar nerve supplies four intrinsic muscles of the foot: abductor hallucis, the flexor digitorum brevis, the flexor hallucis brevis, and the first lumbrical. The cutaneous distribution of the medial plantar nerve is to the anterior two-thirds of the medial sole and medial three and one-half toes, including the nail beds on the dorsum (similar to the cutaneous distribution of the median nerve in the hand).

LATERAL PLANTAR NERVE:

The lateral plantar nerve runs deep to the abductor hallucis muscle as well. It crosses the sole of the foot between the flexor digitorum brevis and quadratus plantae muscles to reach the lateral compartment of the sole, where it divides into the superficial and deep branches. The lateral plantar nerve gives motor supply for the quadratus plantae, the flexor digiti minimi brevis, the adductor hallucis, the dorsal and plantar interossei, three lumbricals, and abductor digiti minimi. The nerve provides cutaneous innervation to the anterior two-thirds of the lateral sole and lateral one and one-half toes (similar to the cutaneous distribution of the ulnar nerve in the hand).

COMMON FIBULAR (PERONEAL) NERVE:

The common fibular (peroneal) nerve runs laterally deep to the lateral collateral ligament of the knee, and winds around the neck of the fibula. It then divides into the deep and superficial branches. The superficial branch supplies the lateral compartment of the leg and sensation from the lateral surface of the leg.

SUPERFICIAL FIBULAR (PERONEAL) NERVE:

The superficial peroneal nerve innervates the peroneus longus and peroneus brevis muscles and the skin over the antero-lateral aspect of the leg along with the greater part of the dorsum of the foot (with the exception of the first web space, which is innervated by the deep peroneal nerve).

DEEP FIBULAR (PERONEAL) NERVE:

Origin: Common peroneal (fibular) nerve (L4-S2).

Branches: Muscular branches, articular branches, lateral branch, medial branch.

Supply: Motor: Tibialis anterior, extensor digitorum longus, extensor hallucis longus, fibularis tertius, extensor digitorum brevis, extensor hallucis brevis muscle. Sensory: Skin of web between the first two toes, ankle joint, tarsal and metatarsophalangeal joints.

SACRAL PLEXUS:

Origin: L4, L5, S1, S2, S3, S4.

Branches: Anterior branches: Nerve to quadratus femoris, nerve to obturator internus, pudendal nerve, nerves to levator ani and external anal sphincter. Posterior branches: Nerve to piriformis , superior gluteal nerve, inferior gluteal nerve, posterior femoral cutaneous nerve, perforating cutaneous nerve, pelvic splanchnic nerves. Terminal branch: Sciatic nerve (divides into tibial and common peroneal nerves).

Supply: Motor: tensor fasciae latae, gluteus maximus, gluteus medius, gluteus minimus, hamstings, adductor magnus, sphincters, levator ani, muscles of the leg and foot. Sensory: skin over the medial surface of the buttock to the middle of the calf muscles, skin of the external genitalia, leg and foot.

Organs: urinary bladder, large intestine, external genitalia.

THE DERMATOMES OF THE LOWER LIMB:

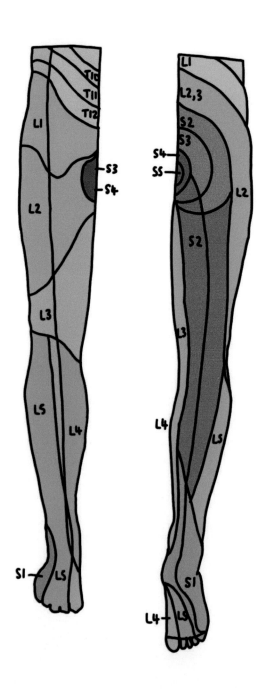

Figure 62. Illustration of the Dermatomes of the Lower Limb.

CHAPTER EIGHTEEN

THE BLOOD SUPPLY OF THE LOWER LIMB

THE BLOOD SUPPLY OF THE LOWER LIMB

ARTERIES OF LOWER LIMB:

FEMORAL ARTERY:

Source: External iliac artery.

Branches: Descending genicular artery, Profunda femoris artery, Superficial epigastric, Superficial circumflex iliac, Superficial external pudendal, Deep external pudendal arteries.

Continuation: Popliteal artery.

Vein: Femoral vein.

Supplies: Anterior compartment of the thigh.

Clinical significance: Cannulation, lacerations, occlusion.

PROFUNDA FEMORIS:

Profunda femoris, also known as the deep artery of the thigh is the largest branch of the femoral artery, which arises 3.5 cm distal to the inguinal ligament. The profunda femoris is initially found lateral to the femoral artery before it passes deep to it towards the medial aspect of the femur. It travels between the pectineus and adductor longus muscles before passing between the adductor longus and adductor brevis muscles. It then descends between the adductor longus and adductor magnus muscles before it pierces the adductor magnus to anastomose with the muscular branches of the popliteal artery. The profunda femoris is the main blood supply to the muscles that extend, flex and adduct the thigh.

POPLITEAL ARTERY:

Source: Femoral artery.

Branches: Anterior tibial artery, Posterior tibial artery, Sural artery, Superior lateral genicular artery, Superior medial genicular artery, Middle genicular artery, Inferior lateral genicular artery, Inferior medial genicular artery.

Supplies: Knee joint, leg muscles.

ANTERIOR TIBIAL ARTERY:

Origin: Popliteal artery.

Branches: Posterior and anterior recurrent tibial, muscular, perforating, and anterior medial and lateral malleolar arteries.

Supply: Proximal tibiofibular joint, knee joint, ankle joint, muscles and skin of the anterior compartment of the leg.

POSTERIOR TIBIAL ARTERY:

Origin: Popliteal artery.

Branches: Circumflex fibular, nutrient, muscular, perforating, communicating, medial malleolar, calcaneal.

Terminal branches: Lateral plantar and medial plantar arteries.

Supply: Proximal end of fibula, tibia, soleus muscle, deep flexors of leg, skin and fascia of posterior leg and heel, muscles of sole of foot.

MEDIAL AND LATERAL PLANTAR ARTERIES:

The plantar arteries supply the skin and muscles of the lateral and medial sides of the foot.

VEINS OF THE LOWER LIMB:

SUPERFICIAL VEINS:

- Great saphenous vein (long saphenous vein)
- Small saphenous vein (short saphenous vein)

DEEP VEINS:

Veins of the foot:

- plantar veins
- dorsal veins

Veins of the leg:

- anterior tibial veins
- posterior tibial veins
- fibular veins

Veins of the knee:

- popliteal vein

Veins of the thigh:

- femoral vein and its tributaries

POPLITEAL VEIN:

The popliteal vein is a deep vein of the leg. It drains blood away from the leg into the femoral vein, which drains blood to the inferior vena cava to return to the right atrium of the heart.

The popliteal vein is formed by the confluence of the deep veins of the leg, i.e. the posterior tibial, anterior tibial and common fibular veins. It also receives venous blood from the superficial vein of the lateral leg, i.e. the short saphenous vein. The short saphenous vein pierces the deep fascia of the leg, and enters the popliteal fossa by passing through the two heads of the gastrocnemius.

The popliteal vein then ascends and passes through the adductor hiatus (an opening formed between the two insertions of the adductor magnus muscle) to become the femoral vein, which passes superiorly and runs in the femoral triangle medial to the femoral artery, which is itself medial to the femoral nerve. The femoral nerve runs underneath the inguinal ligament, and provides motor innervation to the anterior compartment of the thigh.

FEMORAL VEIN:

Drains from: Popliteal vein.

Tributaries: Deep femoral vein, great saphenous vein, lateral circumflex femoral veins, medial circumflex femoral veins.

Drains to: External iliac vein.

Drainage area: Lower limb.

CHAPTER NINETEEN

THE TRUNK AND NECK

THE BONES OF THE TRUNK AND NECK

Now we have covered all of the lower limb, we will start to take a look at the trunk and neck in more detail.

LUMBAR VERTEBRAE, THORACIC VERTEBRAE, CERVICAL VERTEBRAE, AND THE SPINE REGIONS:

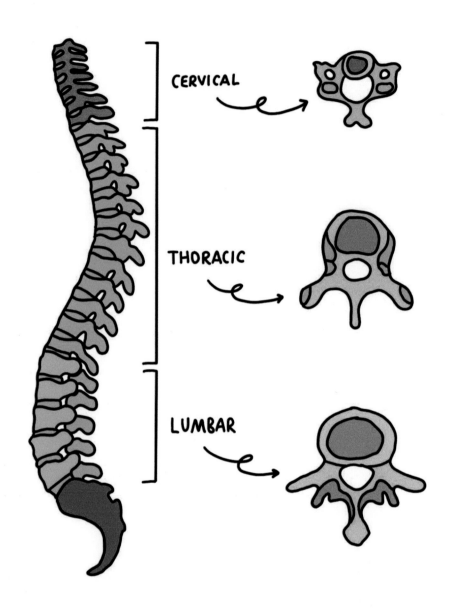

Figure 63. Illustration of the regions of the spine including the lumbar, thoracic and cervical vertebrae.

QUICK FIRE QUIZ!! (Answers at the back of book!)

What is the difference between the lumbar vertebrae and the cervical vertebrae?

....

JOINTS OF THE TRUNK AND NECK

THE INTERVERTEBRAL DISK JOINT AND ZYGAPOPHYSEAL JOINTS:

TYPE	Intervertebral disc joint: Cartilaginous joint; symphysis Zygapophyseal joint: Synovial plane joint, nonaxial, uniplanar
ARTICULAR SURFACES	Intervertebral disc joint: Articular surfaces on vertebral bodies Zygapophyseal joint: Articular surfaces on articular processes
LIGAMENTS	Longitudinal ligaments (anterior, posterior), ligamenta flava, interspinous ligaments, intertransverse ligaments, supraspinous ligaments, nuchal ligament (cervical spine only)
INNERVATION	Intervertebral disc joint: sinuvertebral nerve Zygapophyseal joint: sinuvertebral nerve, medial branch of the posterior ramus of spinal nerve
BLOOD SUPPLY	Segmental arteries
MOVEMENTS	Flexion, extension, lateral flexion and axial rotation of the vertebral column

THE UNCOVERTEBRAL JOINTS:

TYPE	Synovial plane joints
ARTICULAR SURFACES	Uncinate processes C3-C7 and inferior aspect of the respective vertebra above
LIGAMENTS	None
INNERVATION	Spinal nerves C3-C7
BLOOD SUPPLY	Vertebral artery
MOVEMENTS	Slight movements following that of the cervical spine

THE ATLANTOAXIAL JOINTS:

TYPE	Atlantoaxial joint complex: Synovial joint; biaxial
ARTICULAR SURFACES	*Median atlantoaxial joint:* dens of axis (C2), osteoligamentous ring (anterior arch of atlas (C1), transverse ligament of atlas) *Lateral atlantoaxial joints:* inferior articular surface of lateral mass for atlas, superior articular facet of axis
LIGAMENTS	Cruciform ligament (transverse ligament of atlas, superior and inferior longitudinal bands), tectorial membrane, alar ligaments, apical ligament of dens
INNERVATION	Ventral primary ramus of the second cervical spinal nerve
BLOOD SUPPLY	Deep cervical, occipital, vertebral arteries
MOVEMENTS	Principal movement; axial rotation, Limited flexion, extension, lateral flexion

THE ATLANTO-OCCIPITAL JOINT:

TYPE	Synovial ellipsoid joint; biaxial
ARTICULAR SURFACES	Occipital condyles, superior articular facets of atlas
LIGAMENTS	Posterior atlantooccipital ligament, anterior atlantooccipital ligament
INNERVATION	C1 spinal nerve
BLOOD SUPPLY	Anastomosis between deep cervical, occipital and vertebral arteries
MOVEMENTS	Principal movement; Flexion - extension Limited lateral flexion

QUICK FIRE QUIZ!! (Answers at the back of book!)

What are the ligaments of the atlantoaxial joints?

....
....
....

LIGAMENTS OF THE TRUNK AND NECK

THE ANTERIOR LONGITUDINAL LIGAMENT: The anterior longitudinal ligament is a ligament that runs down the anterior surface of the spine. It traverses all of the vertebral bodies and intervertebral discs on their ventral side.

THE POSTERIOR LONGITUDINAL LIGAMENT: The posterior longitudinal ligament is situated within the vertebral canal and extends along the posterior surfaces of the bodies of the vertebrae, from the body of the axis, where it is continuous with the tectorial membrane of atlanto-axial joint, to the sacrum.

THE LIGAMENTUM FLAVUM: runs between the lamina from the axis to the sacrum, the ligamentum flavum connects the laminae and fuses with the facet joint capsules.

THE SUPRASPINOUS LIGAMENT: The supraspinous ligament or supraspinal ligament is a strong fibrous cord that connects together the apices of the spinous processes from the seventh cervical vertebra to 3rd or 4th lumbar vertebrae.

THE LIGAMENTUM NUCHAE: The nuchal ligament is a ligament at the back of the neck that is continuous with the supraspinous ligament.

THE INTERSPINOUS LIGAMENTS: These ligaments extend from the root to the apex of each spinous process. They meet the ligamenta flava in front and blend with the supraspinous ligament behind.

THE INTERTRANSVERSE LIGAMENTS: The intertransverse ligaments are ligaments that are placed between the transverse processes of the spine . In the cervical region they consist of a few irregular, scattered fibers that are often replaced by muscles.

THE ACCESSORY ATLANTOAXIAL LIGAMENT: The accessory atlantoaxial ligament connects the lateral mass of the atlas with the back of the body of the axis and extends to the occipital bone.

THE TRANSVERSE LIGAMENT OF THE ATLAS: The transverse ligament of the atlas stretches between the walls of the vertebral foramen (foramen vertebrale), on the internal surface of the atlas (C1). The ligament crosses the vertebral foramen and directly covers the dens of the axis (C2).

THE TECTORIAL MEMBRANE: The tectoria membrane (TM) is one of two acellular membranes in the cochlea of the inner ear, the other being the basilar membrane (BM).

THE ALAR LIGAMENTS: The alar ligaments are ligaments which connect the dens (a bony protrusion on the second cervical vertebra) to tubercles on the medial side of the occipital condyle. They are short, tough, fibrous cords that attach on the skull and on the axis, and function to check side-to-side movements of the head when it is turned.

THE APICAL LIGAMENT OF THE DENS: The apical ligament is a small ligament that joins the apex (tip) of the dens of C2 to the anterior margin (basion) of the foramen magnum.

THE ANTERIOR ATLANTO-OCCIPITAL MEMBRANE: The anterior atlanto-occipital membrane is a thin membrane that joins the upper border of the anterior arch of the atlas (C1) to the anterior inferior surface of the foramen magnum.

THE POSTERIOR ATLANTO-OCCIPITAL MEMBRANE: Posterior atlanto-occipital ligament and membrane The posterior atlantooccipital membrane (posterior atlantooccipital ligament) is a broad but thin membrane. It is connected above to the posterior margin of the foramen magnum and below to the upper border of the posterior arch of the atlas. It is a continuation from the Ligamentum Flavum.

MUSCLES OF THE TRUNK AND NECK

MUSCLES FLEXING THE TRUNK:

RECTUS ABDOMINIS:

Origin: Pubic symphysis, pubic crest.

Insertion: Xiphoid process, costal cartilages of ribs 5-7

Innervation: Intercostal nerves (T7-T11), subcostal nerve (T12).

Blood supply: Inferior epigastric and superior epigastric arteries; contributions from posterior intercostal, subcostal and deep circumflex arteries.

Function: Trunk flexion, compresses abdominal viscera, expiration.

EXTERNAL OBLIQUE:

Origin: External surfaces of ribs 5-12.

Insertion: Linea alba, pubic tubercle, anterior half of iliac crest.

Action: Bilateral contraction - Trunk flexion, compresses abdominal viscera, expiration. Unilateral contraction - Trunk lateral flexion (ipsilateral), trunk rotation (contralateral).

Innervation: Motor: Intercostal nerves (T7- T11), Subcostal nerve (T12). Sensory: Iliohypogastric nerve (L1).

Blood supply: Lower posterior intercostal arteries, subcostal artery, deep circumflex iliac artery.

INTERNAL OBLIQUE:

Origin: Anterior two-thirds of iliac crest, iliopectineal arch, thoracolumbar fascia.

Insertion: Inferior borders of ribs 10-12, linea alba, pubic crest and pectin pubis (via conjoint tendon).

Action: Bilateral contraction - Trunk flexion, compresses abdominal viscera, expiration. Unilateral contraction - Trunk lateral flexion (ipsilateral), trunk rotation (ipsilateral).

Innervation: Intercostal nerves (T7-T11), subcostal nerve (T12), iliohypogastric nerve (L1), ilioinguinal nerve (L1).

Blood supply: Lower posterior intercostal and subcostal arteries, superior and inferior epigastric arteries, superficial and deep circumflex arteries, posterior lumbar arteries.

PSOAS MINOR:

Origin: Vertebral bodies of T12 and L1 vertebrae.

Insertion: Iliopubic eminence, pecten pubis.

Blood supply: Lumbar arteries.

Innervation: Anterior ramus of spinal nerve L1.

Action: Weak trunk flexion.

PSOAS MAJOR: See page

MUSCLES EXTENDING THE TRUNK:

ERECTOR SPINAE:

Definition: Three groups of deep muscles located on either side of the vertebral column

Function: Bilateral contraction - extension of spine. Unilateral contraction - lateral flexion of spine (ipsilateral)

Three muscles are (from medial to lateral): Spinalis muscles, Longissimus muscles, Iliocostalis muscles.

INTERSPINALES:

Origin: Interspinales cervicis: Superior aspect of spinous processes of vertebrae C3-T1. Interspinales thoracis: Superior aspect of spinous process of vertebrae T2, T11 and T12 (variable). Interspinales lumborum: Superior aspects of spinous processes of vertebrae L2-L5.

Insertion: Interspinales cervicis: Inferior aspect of spinous processes of vertebrae C2-C7. Interspinales thoracis: Inferior aspect of spinous processes of vertebrae T1, T10 and T11. Interspinales lumborum: Inferior aspects of spinous processes of vertebrae L1-L4.

Function: Extension of cervical and lumbar spine.

Innervation: Posterior rami of spinal nerves.

Blood supply: Interspinales cervicis: vertebral artery, deep cervical artery, occipital artery, transverse cervical artery. Interspinales thoracis: superior intercostal artery, posterior intercostal arteries, subcostal artery. Interspinales lumborum: lumbar arteries.

QUADRATUS LUMBORUM:

Origin: Iliac crest, iliolumbar ligament.

Insertion: Inferior border of rib 12, transverse processes of vertebrae L1-L4.

Innervation: Subcostal nerve (T12), anterior rami of spinal nerves L1-L4.

Blood supply: Lumbar, median sacral, iliolumbar and subcostal arteries.

Function: Bilateral contraction - fixes Ribs 12 during inspiration, trunk extension. Unilateral contraction - lateral flexion of trunk (ipsilateral).

MULTIFIDUS:

Origin: Multifidus cervicis: Superior articular processes of vertebrae C4-C7. Multifidus thoracis: Transverse process of thoracic vertebra. Multifidus lumborum: Mammillary processes of lumbar vertebrae, posterior aspect of sacrum, posterior superior iliac spine (PSIS) of ilium and posterior sacroiliac ligament.

Insertion: Lateral aspect and tips of the spinous processes of vertebrae 2-5 levels above origin.

Action: Bilateral contraction: Extension of spine. Unilateral contraction: Lateral flexion of spine (ipsilateral), rotation of spine (contralateral).

Innervation: Medial branches of posterior rami of spinal nerves.

Blood supply: Vertebral artery, deep cervical artery, occipital artery, posterior intercostal arteries, subcostal artery, lumbar ateries and lateral sacral arteries.

SEMISPINALIS:

The superficial muscle layer is composed of the splenius muscles (spinotransversales muscles), which are the splenius capitis and splenius cervicis. These flat muscles are located on the posterolateral aspect of the neck and the posterior upper thorax, overlying the deep muscles of the neck. The splenius muscles both originate from the spinous processes of cervical and thoracic vertebrae.

- The splenius capitis arises from the spinous processes of vertebrae C7-T3 and the lower half of the nuchal ligament. It then passes superolaterally to insert on the mastoid process and the lateral third of the superior nuchal line of the occipital bone.
- The splenius cervicis arises from the spinous processes of vertebrae T3-T6 and inserts onto the transverse processes of vertebrae C1-C3 or C4.

SPLENIUS CAPITIS:

Origin: Spinous processes of vertebrae C7-T3, nuchal ligament.

Insertion: Lateral superior nuchal line of occipital bone, mastoid process of temporal bone.

Action: Bilateral contraction: Extends head/neck.

Unilateral contraction: Lateral flexion and rotation of head (ipsilateral).

Innervation: Lateral branches of posterior rami of spinal nerves C2-C3.

Blood supply: Muscular branches of occipital artery.

SPLENIUS CERVICIS:

Origin: Spinous processes of T3 — T6 vertebrae.

Insertion: Transverse processes of C1 — C3 vertebrae.

Action: Unilateral contraction: lateral flexion and rotation of neck (ipsilateral). Bilateral contraction: extension of neck.

Innervation: Lateral branches of posterior rami of lower cervical spinal nerves.

Blood supply: Vertebral, occipital, superior intercostal, deep cervical, transverse cervical arteries.

MUSCLES ROTATING THE TRUNK:

MULTIFIDUS: See page 155.

ROTATORES:

Origin: Rotatores breves: Transverse processes of vertebrae T2-T12. Rotatores longi: Transverse processes of thoracic vertebrae.

Insertion: Rotatores breves: Laminae/Spinous process of vertebra (1 level above origin). Rotatores longi: Laminae/Spinous process of vertebra (2 levels above origin).

Actions: Bilateral contraction: Extension of thoracic spine. Unilateral contraction: Rotation of thoracic spine (contralateral).

Innervation: Medial branches of posterior rami of spinal nerves.

Blood supply: Dorsal branches of posterior intercostal and lumbar arteries.

SEMISPINALIS: See page 155-156.

INTERNAL OBLIQUE: See page 154.

EXTERNAL OBLIQUE: See page 153-154.

MUSCLES LATERALLY FLEXING THE TRUNK:

QUADRATUS LUMBORUM: See page 155.

INTERTRANSVERSARII:

Origin: Lateral lumbar intertransversarii: Transverse and accessory processes of vertebrae L1-L4. Medial lumbar intertransversarii: Accessory processes of vertebrae L1-L4.

Insertion: Lateral lumbar intertransversarii: Transverse process of succeeding vertebra. Medial lumbar intertransversarii: Mammillary processes of succeeding vertebra.

Action: Assists lateral flexion of the spine; Stabilizes spine.

Innervation: Anterior rami of spinal nerves.

Blood supply: Dorsal branches of lumbar arteries.

EXTERNAL OBLIQUE: See page 153-154.

INTERNAL OBLIQUE: See page 154.

RECTUS ABDOMINIS: See page 153.

ERECTOR SPINAE: See page 154.

MULTIFIDUS: See page 155.

MUSCLES RAISING THE INTRA-ABDOMINAL PRESSURE:

TRANVERSUS ANDOMINIS:

CREMASTER:

Origin: Lateral part: Lower edge of internal abdominal oblique and transversus abdominis muscles, inguinal ligament. Medial part: Pubic tubercle, lateral part of pubic crest.

Insertion: Tunica vaginalis of testis.

Action: Retraction of testis.

Innervation: Genital branch of genitofemoral nerve (L1, L2).

Blood supply: Cremasteric branch of inferior epigastric artery.

EXTERNAL OBLIQUE: See page 153-154.

INTERNAL OBLIQUE: See page 154.

RECTUS ABDOMINIS: See page 153.

MUSCLES OF THE PELVIC FLOOR:

LEVATOR ANI:

Origins: Puborectalis: Posterior surface of bodies of pubic bones (also known as puboanalis). Pubococcygeus: Posterior surface of bodies of pubic bones (lateral to puborectalis). Iliococcygeus: Tendinous arch of interal obturator fascia, Ischial spine.

Insertions: Puborectalis: None (forms 'puborectal sling' posterior to rectum). Pubococcygeus: Anococcygeal ligament, Coccyx, Perineal body and musculature of prostate/ vagina. Iliococcygeus: Anococcygeal ligament, Coccyx.

Innervation: Nerve to levator ani (S4); Pubococcygeus also receives branches via inferior rectal/ perineal branches of Pudendal nerve (S2- S4).

Blood supply: Inferior gluteal, inferior vesical and pudendal arteries.

Function: Stability and support of the abdominal and pelvic organs, resistance against increased intra-abdominal pressure, opening and closing of the levator hiatus.

COCCYGEUS:

Origin: Ischial spine.

Insertion: Inferior end of sacrum, coccyx.

Actions: Supports pelvic viscera, flexes coccyx.

Innervation: Anterior rami of spinal nerves S4 and S5.

Blood supply: Inferior vesical, inferior gluteal and pudendal arteries.

MUSCLES FLEXING THE NECK:

LONGUS COLLI:

Origin: Superior part: Anterior tubercles of transverse processes of vertebrae C3-C5. Intermediate part: Anterior surface of bodies of vertebrae C5-T3. Inferior part: Anterior surface of bodies of vertebrae T1-T3.

Insertion: Superior part: Anterior tubercle of vertebra C1. Intermediate part: Anterior surface of bodies of vertebrae C2-C4. Inferior part: Anterior tubercles of transverse processes of vertebrae C5-C6.

Action: Bilateral contraction: Neck flexion. Unilateral contraction: Neck contralateral rotation, neck lateral flexion (ipsilateral).

Innervation: Anterior rami of spinal nerves C2-C6.

Blood supply: Branches of the vertebral, ascending pharyngeal and inferior thyroid arteries.

STERNOMASTOID:

Origins: Sternal head: superior part of anterior surface of manubrium sterni. Clavicular head: superior surface of medial third of the clavicle.

Insertions: Lateral surface of mastoid process of the temporal bone, lateral half of superior nuchal line of the occipital bone.

Innervation: Accessory nerve (CN XI), branches of cervical plexus (C2-C3).

Functions: Unilateral contraction: cervical spine: neck ipsilateral flexion, neck contralateral rotation. Bilateral contraction: atlantooccipital joint/ superior cervical spine: head/neck extension; Inferior cervical vertebrae: neck flexion; sternoclavicular joint: elevation of clavicle and manubrium of sternum.

Clinical relations: Wryneck, torticollis.

SCALENUS ANTERIOR:

Origin: anterior tubercle of transverse processes of vertebrae C3-C6.

Insertion: anterior scalene tubercle of rib 1, superior border of rib 1 (anterior to subclavian groove).

Innervation: anterior rami of spinal nerves C4-C6.

Blood supply: ascending cervical branch of the inferior thyroid artery.

Function:

- bilateral contraction - neck flexion

- unilateral contraction - neck lateral flexion (ipsilateral), neck rotation (contralateral), elevates rib 1.

MUSCLES FLEXING THE HEAD AND NECK:

LONGUS CAPITIS:

Origin: Anterior tubercles of transverse processes of C3-C6.

Insertion: Basilar part of occipital bone.

Action: Bilateral contraction - head flexion; Unilateral contraction - head rotation (ipsilateral).

Innervation: Anterior rami of spinal nerves C1-C3.

Blood supply: Ascending cervical artery and the inferior thyroid artery.

STERNOMASTOID: See page 158.

MUSCLES EXTENDING THE NECK:

LEVATOR SCAPULAE: See page 35.

SPLENIUS CERVICIS:

Origin: Spinous processes of T3 — T6 vertebrae.

Insertion: Transverse processes of C1 — C3 vertebrae.

Action : Unilateral contraction: lateral flexion and rotation of neck (ipsilateral). Bilateral contraction: extension of neck.

Innervation: Lateral branches of posterior rami of lower cervical spinal nerves.

Blood supply: Vertebral, occipital, superior intercostal, deep cervical, transverse cervical arteries.

MUSCLES EXTENDING THE HEAD AND NECK:

TRAPEZIUS: See page 33-34.

SPLENIUS CAPITIS: See page 156.

ERECTOR SPINAE: See page 154.

MUSCLES LATERALLY FLEXING THE NECK:

SCALENUS ANTERIOR: See page 159.

SCALENUS MEDIUS:

Origin: posterior tubercles of transverse processes of vertebrae C2-C7.

Insertion: superior border of rib 1 (posterior to subclavian groove).

Innervation: anterior rami of spinal nerves C3-C8.

Blood supply: ascending cervical branch of the inferior thyroid artery.

Function: neck lateral flexion, elevates rib 1.

SCALENUS POSTERIOR:

Origin: posterior tubercles of transverse processes of vertebrae C5-C7.

Insertion: external surface of rib 2.

Innervation: anterior rami of spinal nerves C6-C8.

Blood supply: ascending cervical branch of the inferior thyroid artery; superficial cervical artery.

Function: neck lateral flexion, Elevates rib 2.

SPLENIUS CERVICIS: See page 159.

LEVATOR SCAPULAE: See page 35.

STERNOMASTOID: See page 158.

MUSCLES LATERALLY FLEXING THE HEAD AND NECK:

STERNOMASTOID: See Page 158.

SPLENIUS CAPITIS: See page 156.

TRAPEZIUS: See page 33-34.

ERECTOR SPINAE: See page 154.

MUSCLES ROTATING THE NECK:

SEMISPINALIS CERVICIS: See page 155-156.

MULTIFUNDUS: See page 155.

SCALENUS ANTERIOR: See page 159.

SPLENIUS CERVICIS: See page 159.

MUSCLES FLEXING THE HEAD ON THE NECK:

RECTUS CAPITIS ANTERIOR:

Origin: Anterior surface of lateral mass and transverse process of atlas.

Insertion: Inferior surface of basilar part of occipital bone.

Action: Atlantooccipital joint: Head flexion.

Innervation: Anterior rami of spinal nerves C1, C2.

Blood supply: Vertebral artery, ascending pharyngeal artery.

MUSCLES EXTENDING THE HEAD ON THE NECK:

RECTUS CAPITIS POSTERIOR MAJOR:

Origin: Spinous process of axis.

Insertion: Lateral part of inferior nuchal line of occipital bone.

Action: Bilateral contraction at the atlantooccipital joint: Head extension. Unilateral contraction at the atlantoaxial joint: Head rotation (ipsilateral).

Innervation: Suboccipital nerve (posterior ramus of spinal nerve C1).

Blood supply: Vertebral artery and descending branches of the occipital artery.

RECTUS CAPITIS POSTERIOR MINOR:

Origin: Posterior tubercle of atlas.

Insertion: Medial part of inferior nuchal line of occipital bone.

Action: Bilateral contraction - Atlantooccipital joint: Head extension.

Innervation: Posterior ramus of spinal nerve C1 (suboccipital nerve).

Blood supply: Vertebral artery. Occipital artery (via the deep descending branch).

SUPERIOR OBLIQUE:

Origin: Body of the sphenoid bone.

Insertion: Superolateral aspect of eyeball (deep to rectus superior, via trochlea orbitae).

Action: Abducts, depresses, internally rotates eyeball.

Innervation: Trochlear nerve (CN IV).

Blood supply: Ophthalmic artery.

MUSCLES LATERALLY FLEXING THE HEAD ON THE NECK:

RECTUS CAPITIS LATERALIS:

Origin: Superior surface of the transverse process of atlas.

Insertion: Inferior surface of the jugular process of the occipital bone.

Action: Stabilizes the atlanto-occipital joint; head lateral flexion (ipsilateral).

Innervation: Anterior rami of C1-C2 spinal nerves.

Blood supply: Branches of the occipital, vertebral and ascending pharyngeal arteries.

MUSCLES ROTATING THE HEAD AND NECK:

INFERIOR OBLIQUE:

Origin: Orbital surface of maxilla.

Insertion: Inferolateral aspect of eyeball (deep to lateral rectus muscle).

Action: Abducts, elevates, externally rotates eyeball.

Innervation: Oculomotor nerve (CN III).

Blood supply: Ophthalmic artery, infraorbital artery.

RECTUS CAPITIS POSTERIOR MAJOR: See page

MUSCLES ROTATING THE HEAD ON THE NECK:

INFERIOR OBLIQUE: See page 162.

RECTUS CAPITIS POSTERIOR MAJOR: See page 161.

THE NERVES OF THE TRUNK AND NECK

THE CERVICAL PLEXUS:

SENSORY BRANCHES	Lesser occipital nerve, Great auricular nerve, Transverse cervical nerve, Supraclavicular nerve
MOTOR BRANCHES	Muscular branches (to sternocleidomastoid, prevertebral and levator scapulae), Ansa cervicalis, Phrenic nerve
INNERVATION	Lesser occipital nerve - skin of the neck and the scalp posterosuperior to the clavicle Greater auricular nerve - skin over the parotid gland, the posterior aspect of the auricle, and an area of skin extending from the angle of the mandible of the mastoid process Transverse cervical nerve - skin covering the anterior triangle of the neck Supraclavicular nerve - skin over the neck and over the shoulder Ansa cervicalis - infrahyoid muscles Phrenic nerve - diaphragm, mediastinal pleura, pericardium of the heart

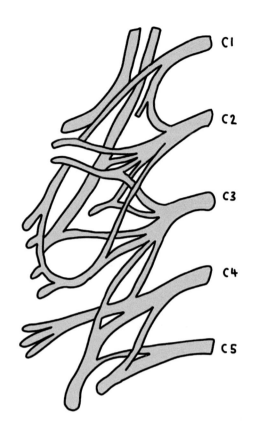

Figure 64. Illustration of the Cervical Plexus.

SUPERFICIAL BRANCHES:

LESSER OCCIPITAL NERVE: The branch is formed by the second cervical nerve (C2) only, and courses to supply the skin of the neck and the scalp posterosuperior to the clavicle. 163

GREATER AURICULAR NERVE: This sensory branch originates from the C2 and C3 nerves. It courses upwards in a diagonal fashion and crosses the sternocleidomastoid muscle onto the parotid gland. It then divides and innervates the skin over the parotid gland, the posterior aspect of the auricle, and an area of skin extending from the angle of the mandible of the mastoid process.

TRANSVERSE CUTANEOUS NERVE OF NECK: The transverse cervical nerve is formed by axons from the second and third cervical nerves. It supplies the skin covering the anterior triangle of the neck. This branch curves around the middle of the posterior border of the sternocleidomastoid muscle and crosses it deep to the platysma muscle.

SUPRACLAVICUALR NERVES: This branch is formed by the C3 and C4 nerves, and it emerges as a common trunk under cover of the sternocleidomastoid muscle and sends small branches to the skin of the neck. Some of those branches of this branch (supraclavicular) also cross the clavicle to supply the skin over the shoulder.

DEEP BRANCHES: the deep branches of the cervical plexus provide motor innervation for the muscles of the neck and the diaphragm.

- MUSCULAR BRANCHES

- LATERAL BRANCHES

- MEDIAL BRANCHES

- PHERENIC NERVE

- LEFT PHERENIC NERVE

- RIGHT PHERENIC NERVE

CHAPTER TWENTY

THE THORAX

THE THORAX

THORACIC VERTEBRAE: Details are given on page 150.

RIBS, COSTAL CARTILLAGE AND THE STERNUM:

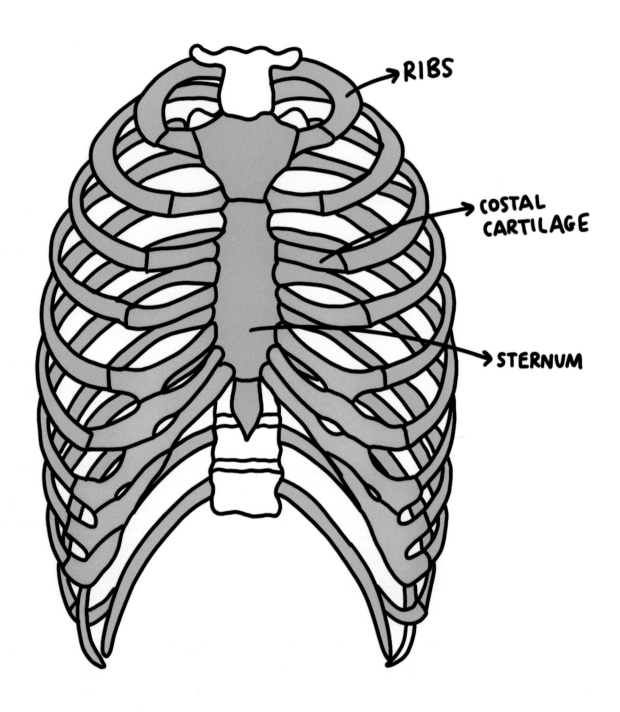

RIBS

COSTAL CARTILAGE

STERNUM

Figure 65. Illustration of the rib cage including the costal cartilage and the sternum.

THE JOINTS OF THE THORAX

COSTOCHONDRAL JOINT:

TYPE	Primary hyaline cartilaginous joint (synchondrosis); synarthrosis
ARTICULAR SURFACES	Sternal (medial) end of rib, lateral end of costal cartilage
LIGAMENTS	None
INNERVATION	Intercostal nerves
BLOOD SUPPLY	Intercostal artery
MOVEMENTS	None

STERNAL JOINTS:

MANUBRIOSTERNAL JOINT:

TYPE	Secondary cartilaginous joint (symphysis)
ARTICULAR SURFACES	Inferior margin of the manubrium of sternum, articular disc, superior margin of sternal body
LIGAMENTS	Manubriosternal ligament
MOVEMENTS	Angulation, anteroposterior displacement

XIPHISTERNAL JOINT:

The xiphisternal joint (or xiphisternal symphysis) is a location near the bottom of the sternum, where the body of the sternum and the xiphoid process meet. It is structurally classified as a synchondrosis, and functionally classified as a synarthrosis. This joint can remain until the middle years of life, but usually ossifies to form a synostosis between the two sternal elements.

COSTOVERTEBRAL JOINT AND THE COSTOTRANSVERSE JOINT:

TYPE	Synovial plane joint
ARTICULAR SURFACES	Costocorporeal joint: Costal demifacets on vertebrae T1-T9, full costal facets on vertebrae T1, T10, T11, T12; heads of ribs 1-12 Costotransverse joint: Tubercle of rib, transverse costal facet on transverse process of numerically equivalent vertebra
LIGAMENTS	Costocorporeal joint: Radiate, intra-articular ligaments (joints 11-12) Costotransverse joint: Costotransverse, superior costotransverse, lateral costotransverse, accessory ligaments
INNERVATION	Lateral branches of the dorsal rami of C8-T11 spinal nerves
BLOOD SUPPLY	Supreme intercostal, posterior intercostal arteries 1-10

MOVEMENTS	Costocorporeal joints: internal rotation and elevation of head of rib
	Costotransverse joints 1-6: internal rotation of neck of rib
	Costotransverse joints 7-10: posteromedial translation of neck of rib

STERNOCOSTAL JOINTS:

TYPE	Sternochondral joint 1: Primary cartilaginous joint (synchondrosis)
	Sternochondral joints 2-7: Synovial planar joints, nonaxial, uniplanar
ARTICULAR SURFACES	Sternal ends of costal cartilages of the true ribs, costal notches on sternum
LIGAMENTS	Radiate sternochondral, xiphichondral and intraarticular sternochondral ligaments
INNERVATION	Intercostal nerve
BLOOD SUPPLY	Internal thoracic artery
MOVEMENTS	Sternochondral joint 1: almost no movement
	Sternochondral joints 2-7: translation, mainly superinferiorly

INTERCHONDRAL JOINTS:

TYPE	6th-9th: Synovial plane joints
	9th-10th: Fibrous joint
ARTICULAR SURFACES	Costal cartilages of 6th and 7th, 7th and 8th, and 8th and 9th ribs
LIGAMENTS	Lateral and medial interchondral ligaments
INNERVATION	Intercostal nerves
BLOOD SUPPLY	Anterior intercostal arteries
MOVEMENTS	Gliding movements

THE LIGAMENTS OF THE THORAX

INTRA-ARTICULAR LIGAMENT: The Intraarticular sternocostal ligament is a horizontal fibrocartilaginous plate in the center of the second sternocostal joint. It connects the tip of the costal cartilage to the fibrous junction between the manubrium and the body of the sternum, dividing the joint into two parts.

RADIATE LIGAMENT OF THE HEAD OF THE RIB: The radiate ligament connects the anterior part of the head of each rib with the side of the bodies of two vertebrae, and the intervertebral fibrocartilage between them. It consists of three flat fasciculi, which are attached to the anterior part of the head of the rib, just beyond the articular surface.

LATERAL COSTOTRANSVERSE LIGAMENT: The lateral costotransverse ligament is a fibrous band that crosses transversely from the posterior surface of the tip of a transverse process of a vertebra to the non-articular part of the tubercle of the corresponding rib.

COSTOTRANSVERSE LIGAMENT: A costotransverse ligament is a short fibrous band that connects a rib with the transverse process of vertebra. They are some of the ligaments that surround the costovertebral joint.

SUPERIOR COSTOTRANSVERSE LIGAMENT: A superior costotransverse ligament is a strong fibrous band that arises from the neck of a rib to the transverse process of the vertebra above.

MUSCLES OF THE THORAX

MUSCLES PRODUCING INSPIRATION:

DIAPHRAGM:

Origin: Sternal part: Posterior aspect of xiphoid process. Costal part: Internal surfaces of lower costal cartilages and ribs 7-12. Lumbar part: Medial and lateral arcuate ligaments (lumbocostal arches), bodies of vertebrae L1-L3 (+intervertebral discs), anterior longitudinal ligament.

Insertion: Central tendon of diaphragm.

Relations: Pleural cavities, pericardial sac, liver, right kidney, right suprarenal gland, stomach, spleen, left kidney, left suprarenal gland.

Openings: Aortic hiatus (aorta, azygos vein, thoracic duct), esophageal hiatus (esophagus, vagus nerve), caval foramen (inferior vena cava) Greater, lesser, least splanchnic nerves, superior epigastric vessels.

Innervation: Phrenic nerves (C3-C5) (sensory innervation of peripheries via 6th-11th intercostal nerves).

Blood supply: Subcostal and lowest 5 intercostal arteries, inferior phrenic arteries, superior phrenic arteries.

Functions: Depresses costal cartilages, primary muscle of breathing (inspiration).

INTERCOSTALS:

Definition: Three sets of rib muscles that occupy the 11 intercostal spaces.

Function: Mechanical support to the thoracic cage, accessory respiratory muscles.

LEVATORES COSTORUM:

Origin: Transverse processes of the C7 — T11.

Insertion: Superior border/external surface of rib one level below origin.

Action: Elevation of the ribs. Rotation of thoracic spine.

Innervation: Posterior rami of spinal nerves T1 — T12.

Blood supply: Posterior intercostal artery.

SERRATUS POSTERIOR SUPERIOR:

Origin: Nuchal ligament, spinous processes of vertebrae C7-T3.

Insertion: Superior borders of ribs 2-5.

Innervation: 2nd-5th Intercostal nerves.

Function: Elevates ribs.

MUSCLES PRODUCING EXPIRATION:
TRANSVERSUS THORACIS:

Origin: Inferoposterior surface of body of sternum and xiphoid process; sternal ends of costal cartilages of ribs 4-7.

Insertion: Internal surface of costal cartilages of ribs 2-6.

Action: Depresses ribs during forced expiration; Supports intercostal spaces and thoracic cage.

Innervation: Intercostal nerves.

Blood supply: Sternal branches of internal thoracic artery.

SUBCOSTALS:

Origin: Internal surface of ribs (near angle of rib).

Insertion: Internal surface of rib (2-3 levels below origin).

Action: Depress ribs during forced expiration; Support intercostal spaces and thoracic cage.

Innervation: Intercostal nerves.

Blood supply: Posterior intercostal artery, musculophrenic artery.

SERRATUS POSTERIOR INFERIROR:

Origin: Spinous processes of vertebrae T11-L2.

Insertion: Inferior borders of ribs 9-12.

Innervation: Anterior rami of spinal nerves T9-T12 (a.k.a. 9th-11th Intercostal nerves + subcostal nerve).

Function: Depresses ribs/ Draws ribs inferoposteriorly.

EXTERNAL OBLIQUE: See Page 153.
INTERNAL OBLIQUE: See Page 154.

TRANSVERSUS ABDOMINIS: See Page 157.

LATISSIMUS DORSI: See Page 44.

QUICK FIRE QUIZ!! (Answers at the end of book!)

What is the action of the subcostal muscles?

....

CHAPTER

TWENTY ONE

THE SPINAL CORD AND NERVOUS SYSTEM

THE SPINAL CORD AND AUTONOMIC NERVOUS SYSTEM:

THE SPINAL CORD:

Definition and function: A part of the central nervous system located in the spinal canal that conveys the information between the brain and the periphery.

Structure and segments

- Composed of an outer layer of white matter and centrally located gray matter.

- Along its length, it consists of the cervical, thoracic, lumbar, sacral, and coccygeal segments.

THE SPINAL NERVES:

31 pair of nerves that emerge from the segments of the spinal cord to innervate the body structures; 8 pairs of cervical, 12 thoracic, 5 lumbar, 5 sacral, and 1 coccygeal pair of spinal nerves.

THE MENINGES:

Definition: Three membranous layers that envelop the brain and the spinal cord.

Meninges and meningeal spaces: Meninges: Dura mater, arachnoid mater, pia mater. Meningeal spaces: Epidural space, subdural space, subarachnoid space.

Function: Mechanical protection of brain and spinal cord, support of cerebral and spinal blood vessels, passage of the cerebrospinal fluid (CSF).

BLOOD SUPPLY OF SPINAL CORD:

Anterior spinal artery

Supplies:

- Anterior gray column of spinal cord
- Lateral gray column of spinal cord
- Central grey matter
- Anterior funiculus
- Lateral funiculus
- Anterior portion of posterior gray matter

Posterior spinal arteries

Supply:

- Posterior portion of posterior gray matter
- Posterior funiculus

Radicular arteries

Supply:

- Entire length of spinal cord
- Spinal nerve roots
- Anterior and posterior spinal arteries

Arterial vasocorona

Supplies:

- pia mater of spinal meninges

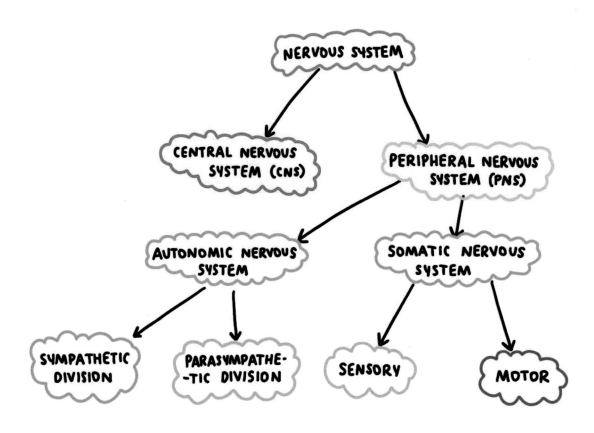

Figure 66. Diagram showing the divisions of the nervous system of the human body.

THE SOMATIC NERVOUS SYSTEM:

The somatic nervous system is the voluntary component of the peripheral nervous system. It consists of all the fibers within cranial and spinal nerves that enable us to perform voluntary body movements (efferent nerves) and feel sensation from the skin, muscles and joints (afferent nerves). Somatic sensation relates to touch, pressure, vibration, pain, temperature, stretch and position sense from these three types of structures.

THE AUTONOMIC NERVOUS SYSTEM:

The autonomic nervous system is the involuntary part of the peripheral nervous system. Further divided into the sympathetic (SANS), parasympathetic (PANS) systems, it is comprised exclusively of visceral motor fibers. Nerves from both these divisions innervate all involuntary structures of the body;

- Cardiac muscle
- Glandular cells
- Smooth muscles present in the walls of the blood vessels and hollow organs.

PARASYMPATHETIC NERVOUS SYSTEM:

The parasympathetic nervous system (PSNS) adjusts our bodies for energy conservation, activating "rest and digest" or "feed and breed" activities. The nerves of the PSNS slow down the actions of cardiovascular system, divert blood away from muscles and increase peristalsis and gland secretion.

SYMPATHETIC NERVOUS SYSTEM:

The sympathetic system (SANS) adjusts our bodies for situations of increased physical activity. Its actions are commonly described as the "fight-or-flight" response as it stimulates responses such as faster breathing, increased heart rate, elevated blood pressure, dilated pupils and redirection of blood flow from the skin, kidneys, stomach and intestines to the heart and muscles, where it is needed.

CHAPTER
TWENTY TWO

THE SKULL

THE BONES OF THE SKULL

SKULL:

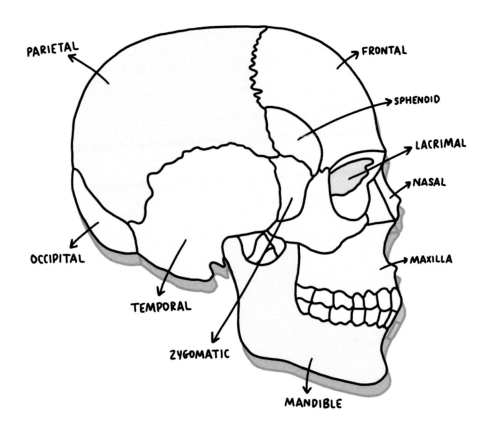

Figure 67. Illustration of the skull labelled.

MANDIBLE:

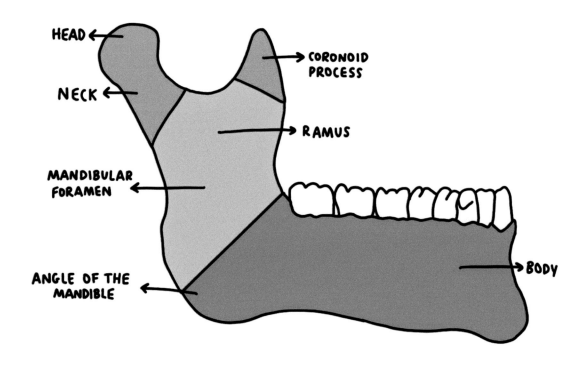

Figure 68. Illustration of the mandible of the jaw labelled.

MUSCLES OF THE SKULL

MUSCLES OF THE FOREHEAD AND EYEBROWS:
OCCIPITOFRONTALIS:

Origin: Frontal belly (frontalis): Skin of eyebrow, muscles of forehead. Occipital belly (occipitalis): (Lateral 2/3 of) superior nuchal line.

Insertion: Epicranial aponeurosis.

Action: Frontal belly: Elevates eyebrows, wrinkles skin of forehead. Occipital belly: Retracts scalp.

Innervation: Frontal belly: Temporal branches of facial nerve (CN VII). Occipital belly: Posterior auricular nerve (branch of facial nerve (CN VII)).

Blood supply: Superficial temporal, ophthalmic, posterior auricular and occipital arteries.

CORRUGATOR SUPERCILII:

Origin: Medial end of superciliary arches, Fibers of orbicularis oculi muscle.

Insertion: Skin above middle of supraorbital margin.

Function: Creates vertical wrinkles over glabella.

Innervation: Temporal branches of facial nerve (CN VII).

Blood supply: Ophthalmic artery, superficial temporal artery.

PROCERUS:

Origin: Nasal bone, (superior part of) lateral nasal cartilage.

Insertion: Skin of glabella, fibers of frontal belly of occipitofrontalis muscle.

Action: Depresses medial end of eyebrow, wrinkles skin of glabella.

Innervation: Temporal, lower zygomatic or buccal branches of facial nerve (CN VII).

Blood supply: Angular and lateral nasal branches of facial artery.

MUSCLES AROUND THE EYE:
ORBICULARIS OCULI:

Origin: Nasal part of frontal bone, frontal process of maxilla, medial palpebral ligament, lacrimal bone.

Insertion: Skin of orbital region, lateral palpebral raphe, superior and inferior tarsal plates.

Actions: Orbital part: Closes eyelids tightly. Palpebral part: Closes eyelids gently. Deep palpebral part: Compresses lacrimal sac.

Innervation: Temporal and zygomatic branches of facial nerve (CN VII).

Blood supply: Maxillary, superficial temporal, facial and ophthalmic arteries.

MUSCLES AROUND THE NOSE:

NASALIS:

Origin: Alar part: Frontal process of maxilla (superior to lateral incisor). Transverse part: Maxilla (superolateral to incisive fossa).

Insertion: Alar part: Skin of ala; Transverse part: Merges with counterpart at dorsum of nose.

Action: Alar part: Depresses ala laterally, dilates nostrils. Transverse part: Wrinkles skin of dorsum of nose.

Innervation: Buccal branch of facial nerve (CN VII).

Blood supply: Superior labial, septal, and lateral nasal branches of facial artery; Infraorbital branch of maxillary artery.

LEVATOR LABII SUPERIORIS ALAQUE NASI:

Origin: The levator labii superioris alaeque nasi muscle originates from the frontal process of the maxilla.

Insertion: The levator labii superioris alaeque nasi inserts into the skin of the lateral part of the nostril and skin of the upper lip.

Action: Contractions of the levator labii superioris alaeque nasi dilates the nostril, elevates the wing of the nose and the upper lip, providing the facial expression that accompanies snarling.

Innervation: The levator labii superioris alaeque nasi is innervated by the zygomatic branches of the facial nerve (CN VII).

Blood supply: Arterial blood is supplied to the levator labii superioris alaeque nasi via the facial artery and the infraorbital branch of the maxillary artery.

DEPRESSOR SEPTI:

Origin: The depressor septi nasi originates from the incisive fossa of the maxilla.

Insertion: The depressor septi nasi inserts into the nasal septum and the posterior aspect of the alar part of the nasalis muscle.

Action: Upon contraction the depressor septi nasi depresses the nasal septum and pulls the wings of the nose downward, constricting the aperture of the nostrils, thus working similarly as the alar part of the nasalis muscle.

Innervation: The depressor septi nasi receives nerve supply from the buccal branch of the facial nerve (CN VII).

Blood supply: The depressor septi nasi is supplied by the superior labial branch of the facial artery.

MUSCLES AROUND THE MOUTH:

ORBICULARIS ORIS:

Origin: Medial aspects of maxilla and mandible, perioral skin and muscles, modiolus.

Insertion: Skin and mucous membrane of lips.

Action: Closes mouth, compresses, and protrudes lips.

Innervation: Buccal branch of facial nerve (CN VII).

Blood supply: Facial artery - Superior and inferior labial arteries. Maxillary artery - Mental and infraorbital arteries. Superficial temporal artery - Transverse facial artery.

BUCCINATOR:

Origin: (External lateral surface of) Alveolar process of maxilla, buccinator ridge of mandible, pterygomandibular raphe.

Insertion: Modiolus, blends with muscles of upper lip.

Function: Compresses cheek against molar teeth.

Innervation: Buccal branch of facial nerve (CN VII).

Blood supply: Buccal artery (maxillary artery), facial artery.

LEVATOR LABII SUPERIORIS ALAEQUE NASI: See previous page.

LEVATOR LABII SUPERIORIS:

Origin: Zygomatic process of maxilla, maxillary process of zygomatic bone.

Insertion: Blends with muscles of upper lip.

Action: Elevates upper lip, exposes maxillary teeth.

Innervation: Zygomatic and buccal branches of facial nerve (CN VII).

Blood supply: Facial artery, infraorbital branch of maxillary artery.

ZYGOMATICUS MAJOR:

Origin: (Posterior part of) Lateral aspect of zygomatic bone.

Insertion: Modiolus, blends with muscles of upper lip.

Function: Elevates and everts angle of mouth.

Innervation: Buccal and zgyomatic branches of facial nerve (CN VII).

Blood supply: Superior labial artery (facial artery).

ZYGOMATICUS MINOR:

Origin: (Anterior part of) Lateral aspect of zygomatic bone.

Insertion: Blends with muscles of upper lip (medial to zygomaticus major muscle).

Action: Elevates upper lip, exposes maxillary teeth.

Innervation: Zygomatic and buccal branches of facial nerve (CN VII).

Blood supply: Superior labial branch of the facial artery.

LEVATOR ANGULI ORIS:

Origin: Canine fossa of maxilla.

Insertion: Modiolus.

Action: Elevates angle of mouth.

Innervation: Zygomatic and buccal branches of facial nerve (CN VII).

Blood supply: Superior labial branch of facial artery, infraorbital branch of maxillary artery.

DEPRESSOR ANGULI ORIS:

Origin: Mental tubercle and oblique line of mandible (continuous with platysma muscle).

Insertion: Modiolus.

Function: Depresses angle of mouth.

Innervation: Buccal and mandibular branches of facial nerve (CN VII).

Blood supply: Inferior labial artery (facial artery); mental artery (maxillary artery).

DEPRESSOR LABII INFERIORIS:

Origin: Oblique line of mandible (continuous with platysma muscle).

Insertion: Skin and submucosa of lower lip.

Action: Depresses lower lip inferolaterally.

Innervation: Mandibular branch of facial nerve (CN VII).

Blood supply: Inferior labial branch of facial artery, mental branch of maxillary artery.

RISORIUS:

Origin: Parotid fascia, buccal skin, zygomatic bone (variable).

Insertion: Modiolus.

Function: Extends angle of mouth laterally.

Innervation: Buccal branch of facial nerve (CN VII).

Blood supply: Superior labial artery (facial artery).

MENTALIS:

Origin: Incisive fossa of mandible.

Insertion: Skin of chin (Mentolabial sulcus).

Action: Elevates, everts and protrudes lower lip, wrinkles skin of chin.

Innervation: Mandibular branch of facial nerve (CN VII).

Blood supply: Inferior labial branch of facial artery, mental branch of the maxillary artery.

QUICK FIRE QUIZ!! (Answers at the back of book!)

What is the innervation of the Zygomaticus major?

....

CHAPTER
TWENTY THREE
THE MANDIBLE AND HYOID

THE BONES OF THE MANDIBLE AND HYOID

THE MANDIBLE: See previous chapter for more information about the mandible.

THE HYOID:

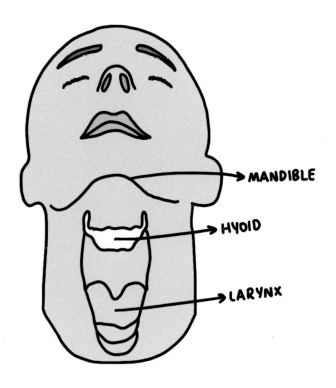

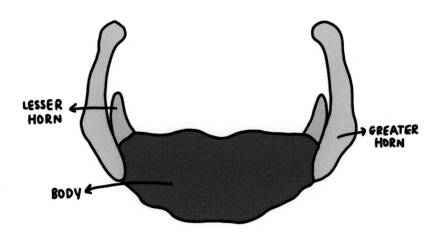

Figure 69. Illustration of the hyoid bone (which is shown in relation to the mandible).

QUICK FIRE QUIZ!! (Answers at the back of book!)

The .... is the situated below the hyoid bone.

Fill in the gap above.

THE JOINTS OF THE MANDIBLE

TEMPOROMANDIBULAR JOINT:

COMPARTMENTS	Superior (translational movement) and inferior compartments (rotational movement)
JOINT CAPSULE	*Limits/borders* - border of mandibular fossa and neck of the mandible above the pterygoid fovea
LIGAMENTS	Collateral, temporomandibular, stylomandibular, and sphenomandibular ligaments
VASCULAR SUPPLY	Deep auricular, superficial temporal, and anterior tympanic arteries
INNERVATION	Mandibular, masseteric, and deep temporal nerves, together with the otic and superior cervical ganglions

THE LIGAMENTS OF THE MANDIBLE

THE SPHENOMANDIBULAR LIGAMENT: The sphenomandibular ligament is a flat, thin band which is attached superiorly to the spina angularis of the sphenoid bone, and, becoming broader as it descends, is fixed to the lingula of the mandibular foramen. The function of the sphenomandibular ligament is to limit distension of the mandible in an inferior direction.

THE STYLOMANDIBULAR LIGAMENT: The stylomandibular ligament is the thickened posterior portion of the investing cervical fascia, which extends from near the apex of the styloid process of the temporal bone to the angle and posterior border of the angle of the mandible, between the masseter and medial pterygoid.

THE MUSCLES OF THE MANDIBLE

MUSCLES PROTRACTING THE MANDIBLE:

LATERAL PTERYGOID:

Origin: Superior head: Infratemporal crest of greater wing of sphenoid bone. Inferior head: Lateral surface of lateral pterygoid plate of sphenoid bone.

Insertion: Superior head: Joint capsule of temporomandibular joint. Inferior head: Pterygoid fovea on neck of condyloid process of mandible.

Action: Bilateral contraction - Protrudes and depresses mandible, stabilizes condylar head during closure; Unilateral contraction - Medial movement (rotation) of mandible.

Innervation: Lateral pterygoid nerve (of mandibular nerve (CN V3)).

Blood supply: Pterygoid branches of maxillary artery, ascending palatine branch of facial artery.

MEDIAL PTERYGOID:

Origin: Superficial part: Tuberosity of maxilla, Pyramidal process of palatine bone; Deep part: Medial surface of lateral pterygoid plate of sphenoid bone.

Insertion: Medial surface of ramus and angle of mandible.

Action: Bilateral contraction - Elevates and protrudes mandible. Unilateral contraction - Medial movement (rotation) of mandible.

Innervation: Medial pterygoid nerve (of mandibular nerve (CN V3)).

Blood supply: Pterygoid branches (maxillary artery, buccal artery, facial artery).

MASSETER:

Origin: Superficial part: maxillary process of zygomatic bone, Inferior border of zygomatic arch (anterior 2/3). Deep part: deep/inferior surface of zygomatic arch (posterior 1/3).

Insertion: Lateral surface of ramus and angle of mandible.

Innervation: Masseteric nerve of mandibular nerve (CN V3).

Blood supply: Masseteric artery.

Function: Elevates and protrudes mandible.

MUSCLES RETRACTING THE MANDIBLE:
TEMPORALIS:

Origin: Temporal fossa (up to inferior temporal line), Temporal fascia.

Insertion: Apex and medial surface of coronoid process of mandible.

Action: Anterior fibres: Elevates mandible. Posterior part: Retracts mandible.

Innervation: Deep temporal branches (of mandibular nerve (CN V3)).

Blood supply: Deep temporal branches of maxillary artery, middle temporal branches from superficial temporal artery.

DIGASTRIC:

Origin: Anterior belly: digastric fossa of mandible. Posterior belly: mastoid notch of temporal bone.

Insertion: Body of hyoid bone (via intermediate tendon and its fibrous sling).

Action: Depresses mandible. Elevates hyoid bone during chewing, swallowing.

Innervation: Anterior belly: mylohyoid nerve (of inferior alveolar nerve) (CN V3). Posterior belly: digastric branch of facial nerve (CN VII).

Blood supply: Anterior belly: facial artery. Posterior belly: occipital artery.

GENIOHYOID:

Origin: Inferior mental spine (inferior genial tubercle).

Insertion: Body of the hyoid bone.

Action: Elevates and draws hyoid bone anteriorly; shortens the mouth floor; widens pharynx.

Innervation: Anterior ramus of spinal nerve C1 (via hypoglossal nerve).

Blood supply: Sublingual branch of the lingual artery.

MUSCLES ELEVATING THE MANDIBLE:

MASSETER: See page 185.

MEDIAL PTERYDOID: See page 185.

TEMPORALIS: See page 185.

MUSCLES DEPRESSING THE MANDIBLE:

DIGATRIC: See page 185.

MYLOHYOID:

Origin: Mylohyoid line of mandible.

Insertion: Mylohyoid raphe, body of hyoid bone.

Action: Forms floor of oral cavity, elevates hyoid bone and floor of mouth, depresses mandible.

Innervation: Nerve to mylohyoid (of inferior alveolar nerve (CN V3)).

Blood supply: Sublingual, inferior alveolar and submental arteries.

GENIOHYOID: See page 185-186.

PLATYSMA:

Origins: Skin/fascia of infra- and supraclavicular regions.

Insertion: Lower border of mandible, skin of buccal/cheek region, lower lip, modiolus, orbicularis oris muscle.

Innervation: Cervical branch of facial nerve (CN VII).

Blood supply: submental artery (facial artery), suprascapular artery (thyrocervical trunk).

Actions: Depresses mandible and angle of mouth, tenses skin of lower face and anterior neck.

MUSCLES DEPRESSING THE HYOID:

STERNOHYOID:

Origin: Manubrium of sternum, medial end of clavicle.

Insertion: Inferior border of body of hyoid bone.

Action: Depresses hyoid bone (from elevated position).

Innervation: Anterior rami of spinal nerves C1-C3 (via ansa cervicalis).

Blood supply: Superior thyroid artery.

STERNOTHYROID:

Origin: Posterior surface of manubrium of sternum, Costal cartilage of rib 1.

Insertion: Oblique line of thyroid cartilage.

Action: Depress the larynx.

Innervation: Anterior rami of C1-3 (via the ansa cervicalis).

Blood supply: Superior thyroid and lingual arteries.

THYROHYOID:

Origin: Oblique line of thyroid cartilage.

Insertion: Inferior border of body and greater horn of hyoid bone.

Action: Depresses hyoid bone. Elevates larynx.

Innervation: Anterior ramus of spinal nerve C1 via hypoglossal nerve (CN XII).

Blood supply: Branches of lingual and superior thyroid arteries.

OMOHYOID:

Origin: Inferior belly: superior border of scapula near the suprascapular notch. Superior belly: intermediate tendon.

Insertion: Inferior belly: intermediate tendon. Superior belly: body of hyoid bone.

Action: Depresses and retracts hyoid and larynx. Tenses carotid sheath.

Innervation: Anterior rami of spinal nerves C1-C3 (via ansa cervicalis).

Blood supply: Superior thyroid artery.

MUSCLES ELEVATING THE HYOID:
STYLOHYOID:

Origins: Styloid process of temporal bone.

Insertions: Body of hyoid bone.

Action: Elevates and draws hyoid bone posteriorly.

Innervation: Stylohyoid branch of facial nerve (CN VII).

Blood supply: Branches from the facial, occipital and posterior auricular arteries.

DIGASTRIC: See page 185.

MYLOHYOID: See page 186.

GENIOHYOID: See page 185-186.

QUICK FIRE QUIZ!! (Answers at the back)

What is the insertion of the platysma muscle?

....

CHAPTER
TWENTY FOUR
THE ANSWERS

ANSWERS:

CHAPTER ONE:

In the anatomical position which direction are the palms facing?

    A. Anteriorly

What sections does the frontal (coronal) plane divide the body into?

    B. Anterior and Posterior

The elbow is.......Proximal................. to the hand.

The hand is.............Distal................. to the elbow.

The shoulder is.............Superior.................... to the hand.

The nose sits.............Anteriorly................. on the body.

What is the movement in which a limb moves away from the midline of the body?

    A. Abduction

CHAPTER TWO:

Name 3 bones that are included within the axial skeleton.

Any 3 from the following: The skull, middle ear ossicles (3 in each ear), hyoid bone in the neck, bones of vertebral column (spine), chest bone (sternum), and ribs (12 pairs).

Name and explain some examples of different types of bone.

Any from the following: Short bones (e.g. wrist bones), Long bones (e.g. Femur), Flat bones (e.g. Bones of skull), Irregular bones (eg. Vertebrae).

Name a type of synovial joint and give one example of this type of joint.

Any from the following:

Pivot joint: Only allows movement around one single axis eg. Between C1 and C2 of vertebrae, allows rotation of neck.

Ball and socket joint: A joint where a ball shaped surface fits into a cup like surface. Movement is multiaxial. Eg. Shoulder.

Condyloid or ellipsoid joint: A joint where an ovoid surface fits into an elliptical cavity. This allows movement in 2 different planes. Eg. Joint between radius and carpal bones of the wrist.

Plane joint: Bones are able to slide over one another. Eg. In between tarsal bones.

Saddle joint: The reciprocating surfaces are usually concave and convex which means they can slide against one another. Eg. Thumb joint.

Hinge joint: A joint that allows movement in one direction and usually one plane (it works just like the hinge on a door!) eg. Elbow.

Name and explain an example of a second-class lever within the human body.

Second class lever: The load is in the middle between the fulcrum and the effort. This lever can be found in the ankle area when you stand on tiptoes, can be used when jumping or pushing off. (Any other example that would work in this context is also acceptable!)

Are skeletal muscles striated?

    A. Yes

Name 3 different types of muscle fibre arrangements...

Any from...

Convergent, Unipennate, Bipennate, Multipennate, Circular, Fusiform, Parallel.

What is a muscle fibre made up of? Choose one answer!

    B. Myofibrils

CHAPTER THREE:

What bones are included within the pectoral girdle?

    A. Scapula and Clavicle

What joints are included within the pectoral girdle?

    B. Sternoclavicular and Acromioclavicular

What muscle attaches to the subscapular fossa?

The subscapularis muscle.

Where does the sternal end of the clavicle attach to?

    C. The sternum

Name a ligament involved within the sternoclavicular joint:

One from the following:

Intrinsic ligaments: anterior and posterior sternoclavicular ligaments

Extrinsic ligaments: interclavicular and costoclavicular ligaments

Name a movement produced by the acromioclavicular joint.

One of the following:

Protraction – retraction
Elevation – depression
Axial rotation

Name 3 ligaments that are found within the pectoral girdle.

Any 3 from the following:

Anterior sternoclavicular ligament, Posterior sternoclavicular ligament, Interclavicular ligament, Costoclavicular ligament, Coracoclavicular ligament, Acromioclavicular ligament.

What muscles medially rotate the pectoral girdle?

Rhomboid major, Rhomboid minor, Pectoralis minor, Levator scapulae.

What is the action, origin, insertion, and innervation for the Trapezius upper fibres?

Origin: Medial third of the superior nuchal line, external occipital protuberance.

Insertion: Lateral third of clavicle.

Action: Scapulothoracic joint: draws scapula superomedially. Atlantooccipital joint: extension of head and neck, lateral flexion of head and neck (ipsilateral). Atlantoaxial joint: rotation of head (contralateral).

Innervation: Motor: accessory nerve (CN XI). Motor/Sensory: ventral rami of spinal nerves C3-C4 (via cervical plexus).

CHAPTER FOUR:

Name (and palpate if you can!) 2 bony landmarks on the humerus bone.

Any from the image shown below:

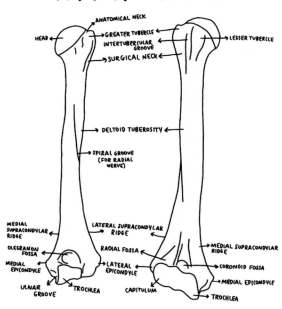

Can you identify a bony landmark on the lateral side of the scapula?

Any from the diagram shown below:

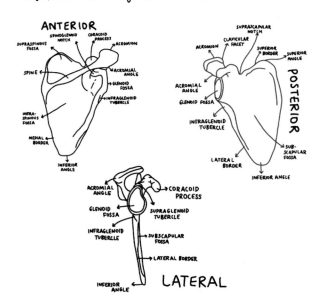

Name one of the ligaments involved in the shoulder joint.

Any from the following:

Superior glenohumeral, middle glenohumeral, inferior glenohumeral, coracohumeral, transverse humeral.

What does the coracohumeral ligament join together?

This ligament joins the coracoid process to the humerus bone.

Name 2 muscles that medially rotate the shoulder joint.

Any two of the following:

Subscapularis, Teres major, Latissimus dorsi, Pectoralis major, Deltoid (anterior fibres).

CHAPTER FIVE:

Name the 2 bones that are present in the forearm.

Ulna and Radius

What side does the ulna face when the forearm is supinated? (Palm up)

Posteriorly

Can you name the bones (there are 2!) that articulate with the humerus to create the elbow joint?

Ulna and Radius

What movements are produced at the elbow joint?

Flexion – Biceps brachii, Brachialis, Brachioradialis muscles
Extension – Triceps brachii muscle.

Name and explain the location of 2 ligaments found within the elbow joint.

Ulnar collateral ligament: This ligament connects the humerus to the ulna medially (on the inside of the elbow).

Radial collateral ligament: This ligament connects the humerus to the radius bone laterally (on the outside of the elbow).

Annular ligament: This ligament encircles the head of the radius and is attached to the ulna; this allows the head of the radius to be kept by the head of the ulna for smoother articulation with the humerus bone.

Quadrate ligament: This ligament runs from the inferior border of the annular ligament to the neck of the radius.

What is the action of the brachialis muscle?

Strong flexion of forearm at the elbow joint.

CHAPTER SIX:

What does the annular ligament do?

This ligament encircles the head of the radius and is attached to the ulna; this allows the head of the radius to be kept by the head of the ulna for smoother articulation with the humerus bone.

What is the blood supply of the inferior radioulnar joint?

Anterior interosseous, posterior interosseous and ulnar arteries.

What does the triangular fibrocartilage complex act as?

It acts as a stabilizer for the ulnar aspect of the wrist.

Name 2 of the muscles that are supinators of the forearm.

Any 2 from: Supinator, Biceps Brachii, Brachioradialis.

Name 2 of the muscles that are pronators of the forearm.

Any 2 from: Pronator Teres, Pronator Quadratus, Brachioradialis.

CHAPTER SEVEN:

Can you name the 8 bones which make up the carpus?

Scaphoid, Lunate, Triquetrum, Pisiform, Trapezium, Trapezoid, Capitate, Hamate

What movements are created from the intercarpal joints?

Flexion-extension, abduction-adduction, circumduction

Name one ligament involved in the movements of the wrist.

One from any of the following:

Palmar radiocarpal ligament, dorsal radiocarpal ligament, palmar ulnocarpal ligament, ulnar collateral ligament, radial collateral ligament, interosseous ligament, palmar intercarpal ligament, dorsal intercarpal ligament

CHAPTER EIGHT:

What way are the metacarpals labelled 1-5?

Left to Right.

How many bones are there included within the phalanges on each hand?

14 in each hand.

What is the innervation of the interphalangeal joint?

Proper palmar digital nerves.

What is the insertion for the Abductor Pollicis Longus muscle?

Base of metacarpal bone 1, (trapezium bone).

CHAPTER NINE:

What is the origin of the Axillary Nerve?

Posterior cord of brachial plexus (C5-C6).

What is the area that C7 covers in Dermatomes?

C7 - hand, middle finger.

CHAPTER TEN:

No questions.

CHAPTER ELEVEN:

Which bones are included within the pelvic girdle?

    A. The innominate and the Sacrum.

Can you name a structure found within the innominate?

Any from the diagram shown.

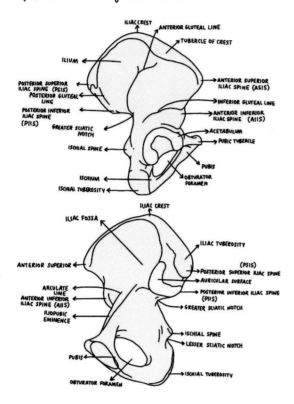

What is the innervation of the sacroiliac joint?

S1-S2 spinal nerves, superior gluteal nerve, obturator nerve, lumbosacral trunk.

Can you name 1 or 2 ligaments that are involved in the lumbosacral joint?

Iliolumbar ligament, lateral lumbosacral ligament

Describe the position of the superior posterior sacrococcygeal ligament.

This ligament arises from the margin of the sacral hiatus and attaches to the dorsal surface of the coccyx.

CHAPTER TWELVE:

The femur is the ....largest..................... **and** ....strongest........................... **bone in the human body.**

What is the blood supply of the hip joint? Can you name at least one main artery?

Medial and lateral circumflex femoral arteries, obturator artery, superior and inferior gluteal arteries.

Describe the pathway of the transverse ligament of the acetabulum.

The transverse ligament of the hip bridges the acetabular notch (located anteroinferiorly along the margin of the acetabulum) and joins the two ends of the acetabular labrum, thus forming a complete ring. Beneath it (through the acetabular foramen) pass nutrient vessels which enter the ligamentum teres which arises from the transverse ligament.

What is the insertion of the obturator internus?

Medial surface of greater trochanter of femur.

CHAPTER THIRTEEN:

Can you name a bony landmark on the tibia bone?

Any from the diagram shown below:

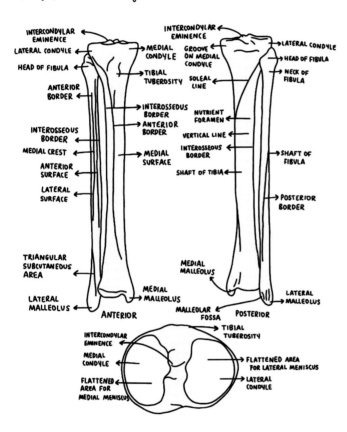

What are the articular surfaces of the patellofemoral joint?

Tibiofemoral joint: lateral and medial condyles of femur, tibial plateaus
Patellofemoral joint: patellar surface of femur, posterior surface of patella.

Describe the location of the medial meniscus.

The medial meniscus is a fibrocartilage semi-circular band that spans the knee joint medially, located between the medial condyle of the femur and the medial condyle of the tibia.

CHAPTER FOURTEEN:

Can you describe the position of the posterior ligament of the fibular head?

The posterior ligament of the head of the fibula is a part of the knee. It is a single thick and broad band, which passes obliquely upward from the back of the head of the fibula to the back of the lateral condyle of the tibia.

CHAPTER FIFTEEN:

Can you name any bony landmarks of the talus bone?

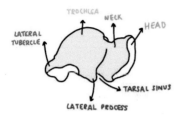

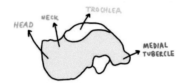

What is the blood supply for the talocrural joint?

Anterior tibial, posterior tibial and fibular arteries

Can you describe the difference between the lateral collateral ligament complex and the deltoid ligament?

The lateral collateral ligament (complex) of the ankle is a set of three ligaments that resist inversion of the ankle joint. They are more commonly injured than the medial collateral (deltoid) ligament of the ankle. They run from the lateral malleolus of the fibula to the talus and calcaneus. This complex is made up of the ATFL (anterior talofibular ligament), the PTFL (posterior talofibular ligament), and the Calcaneofibular ligament. The deltoid ligament is a strong, flat, triangular band, attached, above, to the apex and anterior and posterior borders of the medial malleolus. The deltoid ligament is composed of: 1. Anterior tibiotalar ligament 2. Tibiocalcaneal ligament 3. Posterior tibiotalar ligament 4. Tibionavicular ligament. These ligaments sit medially on the ankle.

What is the insertion of the peroneus longus?

Superficial fibular nerve (L5, S1).

CHAPTER SIXTEEN:

Name 3 bones present in the foot.

There are 26 bones of the foot which **consist** of eight distinct types, including the tarsals, metatarsals, phalanges, cuneiforms, talus, navicular, and cuboid bones. Any mention of any of these bones would be okay.

What is the blood supply for the interphalangeal joint?

Digital branches of plantar arch.

What is the location of the dorsal talonavicular ligament?

This ligament connects the neck of the talus to the dorsal surface of the navicular bone.

CHAPTER SEVENTEEN:

No questions.

CHAPTER EIGHTEEN:

No questions.

CHAPTER NINETEEN:

What is the difference between the lumbar vertebrae and the cervical vertebrae?

Thoracic vertebrae are the twelve vertebrae which allow attachment sites for all ribs. Lumbar vertebrae consist of five cylindrical bones that make the spine in the lower back of the body. Cervical, thoracic, and lumbar are three groups of vertebrae in the vertebral column.

What are the ligaments of the atlantoaxial joints?

Posterior atlantooccipital ligament, anterior atlantooccipital ligament.

CHAPTER TWENTY:

What is the action of the subcostal muscles?

Depress ribs during forced expiration; Support intercostal spaces and thoracic cage.

CHAPTER TWENTY-ONE:

No questions.

CHAPTER TWENTY-TWO:

What is the innervation of the Zygomaticus major?

Buccal and zgyomatic branches of facial nerve (CN VII).

CHAPTER TWENTY-THREE:

The ....Larynx........................... is the situated below the hyoid bone.

What is the insertion of the platysma muscle?

Lower border of mandible, skin of buccal/cheek region, lower lip, modiolus, orbicularis oris muscle.

CHAPTER
TWENTY FIVE
REFERENCES

REFERENCES:

Soames, R. and Palastanga, N., 2018. Anatomy and Human Movement. Elsevier.

H., B. and J., G., 2017. Principles of Anatomy and Physiology, 15E, Global Edition. John Wiley and Sons, Incorporated.

Biel, A., 2014. Trail Guide to the Body. Books of Discovery.

Kenhub. 2021. Learn human anatomy the fastest, most engaging and guided way @Kenhub. (ONLINE) Available at: https://www.kenhub.com. (Accessed 28 August 2021).

HERE ARE SOME SPARE PAGES TO ADD SOME NOTES TO:

HERE ARE SOME SPARE PAGES TO ADD SOME NOTES TO:

....

....

....

....

....

....

....

....

....

....

....

....

....

....

....

....

....

....

....

....

....

HERE ARE SOME SPARE PAGES TO ADD SOME NOTES TO: